THE UNBECOMING

THE UNBECOMING

Stories, thoughts, and inspiration on the miraculous journey of healing the mind and body and uncovering our true selves.

Lauren Giammarco

NEW DEGREE PRESS

THE UNBECOMING

Stories, thoughts, and inspiration on the miraculous journey of healing the mind and body and uncovering our true selves.

ISBN

979-8-88504-115-7 *Paperback*

979-8-88504-743-2 *Kindle Ebook*

979-8-88504-222-2 *Digital Ebook*

Gianna and Alessandra, the girls who made me an auntie. May you always feel at home in your own hearts and know how bright you shine just by being yourselves.

Friendship is often disguised as an Earth angel. Patsy, you are one of them.

Pete and Lisa, this book will be obvious I am the middle child. Thanks for a lifetime of being nonjudgmental.

Mom and Dad, of the hundreds of things I have declared I'm doing without ever actually completing them, this book is proof your belief in my writing since I was a child helped me through this process of book writing.

To my love, Matt. Thank you for reminding me that with a little humor and humility, you can master life.

And to everyone reading this book:

May you always know that everything you need is already inside you.

(Although I still recommend the inside of this book, so please continue on.)

CONTENTS

FOREWORD

I met Lauren through my company CFS Health, an online recovery program that helps people dealing with chronic illness get healthy and start living again.

When I first met Lauren, to say she was struggling was an understatement: barely living is how I would describe it. Her story is a true hero's journey. I have seen her go from the depths of despair, not knowing how to get out of it, to living a full life she absolutely loves.

She is true leader, one who walks the talk, combining her skills as a health/well-being/home environment and professional organizing consultant and her own personal self-healing journey. Lauren offers sound, often effective tools to encourage well-being and living an authentic life. Her book offers reassurance for those in a dark time and inspiration for those who are ready to take their health and life to the next level.

Lauren thank you for stepping up and being a voice for those who need it right now.

CFS Health's mission is to breed healthier, more balanced, whole individuals who do more of what they love and love more of what they do. This inspires others in their circle to do the same. We create a ripple effect all around the world far greater than we will ever know. Lauren is not only part of this ripple effect, but through her work, she is creating her own.

Enjoy the read.
Toby Morrison

AUTHOR'S NOTE

I would like to start off with a confession. I am a recovering perfectionist.

I wore it as a badge of honor most of my adult life. Obsessing over details, holding on tight to outcomes, never wanting to make mistakes. Overthinking, overanalyzing, hustling, running on a hamster wheel going nowhere. Literally exhausting myself confusing perfectionism with excellence.

As a child, perfectionism was the protective shield I created to mask my insecurities and fears. I could not go to sleep unless my bedroom was perfectly clean and organized, and I would agonize over a bad grade in math or not doing well in dance class in comparison to my peers.

As an adult, my self-worth was tied up in this perfectionist game I was playing, fueled by the external validation of others.

"Perfection is a self-persecutory myth. You do not have to be perfect to be safe, loved, or in the present moment. A mistake does not mean you are a mistake."

PETE WALKER

Carrying this weight of perfectionism around on your shoulders will trick you into thinking that you are not worthy unless you are perfecting. And this will become hard to carry.

This perfectionism became a weight. It was almost as if someone planted an anchor in my body when I was asleep, and it stayed there like a dead weight.

I could not lift it, so I carried it with me instead.

This heavy weight and I began moving through life together. I allowed it to be there without questioning its existence, without asking what it needed or becoming curious about what it wanted me to notice. The more I ignored its presence, the heavier it became until the carrying became a wanting and longing, a need to escape it.

So I became immersed in escape and distraction.

You never think to ask how you can thrive, become at peace in life, and live unapologetically as yourself when you are carrying a weight you continuously hide and distract from.

The emotional weight slowly began to manifest itself in occasional physical symptoms, masking itself in pain, fatigue, and stomachaches.

When my marriage ended, a relationship that extended far beyond what my emotional capacity could endure, I became obsessed with perfecting my physical strength as a distraction from processing my emotions. I began spending all my free time on weekends hiking mountains: four to five thousand feet up, maybe more. The higher the climb, the more I wanted to tackle it.

There is a flow to follow when immersing ourselves in nature and an open mindset to grasp as you follow her lead. When I started these more challenging hikes, I was missing that gentle and peaceful dance. I was instead convinced I could take on anything and became fixated on challenging myself more and more with harder climbs rather than simply enjoying the process.

I had mistakenly used physical strength to keep climbing that perfectionist mountain and the truth is it was taking me farther and farther away from my true self: the little girl on the inside who loved to daydream, journal, and simply be and the adult who found her peace among the trees.

Yet I allowed the weight of perfectionism to become my clutch until my health, my livelihood, and my physical strength was pulled from my feet.

In December of 2019 I became chronically ill and spent a year regaining my strength after experiencing debilitating fatigue, flulike symptoms, and pain that lasted for months. I was diagnosed with ME/CFS, clinically known as myalgic encephalomyelitis/chronic fatigue syndrome. Researchers at UC San Diego Health in their article "For ME/CFS Patients, Viral Immunities Come at a Devastating, Lifelong Cost" characterize this condition as a neuroimmune disorder citing the "cell danger response theory" which is the consequence of the natural healing cycle in our bodies that is blocked by disruptions at the metabolic and cellular levels.

My body was failing to recover after the slightest physical or mental exertion. It was as if my body finally shouted at me to stop living out of alignment and tune in toward myself.

If you have ever experienced the heartache that follows a chronic illness diagnosis or know someone who has, it can quickly become a place of despair and fear. It was one of the darkest times in my life.

Or maybe you haven't experienced the physical manifestation of symptoms in your body from stress, living out of alignment with your true self, or carrying a heavy weight, but you have known despair through emotional triggers, life stressors, or anxiety. I am here to tell you this or any major setback in your life, does not have the final say in how your life can unfold.

You are worthy of a life that is in full service of you.

Ask yourself what gifts you might be hiding that are waiting to rise to the surface of your life. How can you begin to uncover these hidden gems? The journey to that realization and the magic of its unfolding piece by piece, layer by layer, is undoubtedly the path to freedom.

This illness helped me find my way back to me, my own path to freedom. It helped me to shed all the layers that were keeping me from fully standing in my truth. It allowed me to stop climbing that never-ending mountain and become still. Something wonderful happened despite the state of things in and around me. Despite my past choices, my health crisis, and the self-sabotaging judgments I have carried I feel deeply, but I have learned to heal deeply.

When you mask yourself for fear of being seen as you truly are, you will lose pieces of yourself that are your most precious parts.

I was moved to write this book as I became committed to regaining my strength, taking ownership of my life, creating a new path, and leaning into self-love and compassion for my journey while overcoming perfectionism, false identities, and self-sabotage. Each chapter of this book tells a story and shows how uncovering your true self is ultimately your path to freedom.

The steps I took to get there and rebuild my health are the principles I share in this book. In a world that is constantly pulling you in different directions, creating a storm of chaos where you find yourself pulled farther away from what your heart truly wishes. Imbalance and disease can take over yet you can choose to empower yourself to move through this.

I am not an expert on these themes, nor a doctor or therapist. I am a human who feels deeply and is having a human experience. I am sharing the journey that uncovered the realization that we can experience both sadness and happiness, loss and gain, and darkness and light. The balance of things creates harmony when you decide to fully dance in your own light and release the stories that no longer serve you. I am sharing my story of how healing from chronic illness brought to light the buried parts of myself that needed the most illumination: the parts of myself that I felt needed masking and hiding and had immense shame around.

As I started to embark on my healing journey, I began to recount each stage of my life from my earliest childhood memories up until the current moment. Sifting through my life, looking back on it, suddenly as if looking through a clear glass, I began to connect the dots. I saw clearly how each choice was either moving toward the most authentic version of myself or pulling me away.

How you can begin to connect these dots within your own life, witnessing the choices that may have found you feeling farther from your truth, is the message within this book.

The good news is you can find yourself again. You can rebuild, realign, and move forward.

Before you begin reading this book, I invite you to take a moment to tune into yourself. Take a breath, find a place to sit alone, cross-legged on the floor, open and vulnerable to how it feels to connect with yourself. Ask any weight you may be carrying the one question that it needs to be lifted—finally:

"What are you asking me to stop carrying?"

Then the real work begins. There is no timeline or certainty on this journey back to our true self, but you will slowly notice days when you feel lighter—you will not need to escape. And days where sitting in stillness—in the quiet, just being—is more than enough.

Please remember that freeing yourself from fear, from the way you believe things should be, from suffering, and from all illusion is the path to true liberation that will drop all weights we carry.

Today, take a breath and ask yourself what needs to stop being carried so you can walk without weight into the truest, most loving version of *you*.

Meet yourself there, always.

If there are oceans inside you wild with love, pain, secrets, and fears among endless star-filled skies and a thousand perfect storms, this book is for you.

I wrote this book for the empaths, the wanderers, the dreamers. The ones who have overcome, who are moving through, and who are learning their way. Read this book if you are beginning to question your place in the world and have begun to slowly outgrow who you once were. You are right on track! I want you to know being yourself is the path to your freedom. The beauty of your truth is how you wear who you are: the rarest, truest form of beauty.

In this tainted world, we can become the balance, the grounded force, the gift we are searching for.

Take a breath, a long breath, and know that you are home in your own heart.

May you find comfort, inspiration, humor, and healing within the chapters of this book. And may your empathetic hearts remain open, protected, nourished, and full.

1

HIDDEN MESSAGES

CHAPTER 1

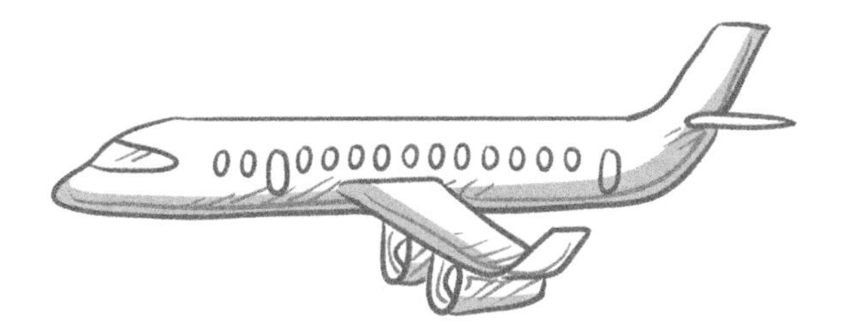

"Never trust your fears. They don't know your strengths."

ATHENA SINGH

I had a 5:00 a.m. direct flight out of Boston heading to Dallas on a rainy September morning. One week prior I had accepted a sales position that required frequent domestic travel, despite my crippling fear of flying. That was the day I uncovered what it meant to begin facing your fears.

It was the kind of fear that would settle into my chest eventually, making its way down to my stomach, where it would begin brewing and collecting her master plan of taking over my thoughts. Before I could realize, she would then take up residence in every part of my body, settling in and pulling up a chair to stay awhile to make certain I knew it had arrived. I allowed panic, anxiety, obsessive thinking, and feeling wildly uncomfortable to live there every time.

The biology behind this intrinsic human emotion is perfectly crafted and designed to protect us from a perceived threat. Like feeling as though a wild tiger is running toward us. In an article titled "Your Stone Age Brain" by *Psychology Tools*, the "hardware" underlying these responses in humans is said to be unchanged over the last 200,000 years. Our protective brain prepares our body for movement, because clearly, we would have to run like the wind from this tiger or bear all while launching stress hormones like rocket ships throughout our body. Just in case we did not get the memo that we are in danger, the protection plan does not end there. Our body also makes sure our sympathetic nervous system is triggered which causes our adrenal glands to release adrenaline into our bloodstream, and before we know it, our hearts are pumping and we are out of breath and feeling faint.

This is all well and good if in fact we have landed ourselves in a situation in which a bear or tiger is chasing us however when this response is being fired away in our bodies when a threat is quite low it can be an uncomfortable experience.

I had decided my love for travel outweighed my fear of flying. I had a love for travel and it was something I had done frequently whether road tripping or flying. I told myself the only way to overcome this fear was to face it: to lean into that glimmer of courage and hope fear could not seem to quiet with the rationalization that the more I did it the less of a chance I had at being terrified. It was muscle memory so to speak.

I have always been both a wandering soul at heart and in love with the safety and comforts of home, a contradiction I take total ownership of. It felt somewhat rebellious and exciting to make a choice to step out of that box of safety and control and lean into courage and appreciation.

For years I had been practicing playing the appreciation game whenever a fear-based thought came up. I learned this from spiritual teacher and author Gabby Bernstein. This practice allows us to redirect our thoughts when a fear arises and redirects momentum of that fear-based thought within minutes.

This practice allowed me to release the fear, and I also began to understand that by redirecting my thoughts, I could then focus more on what I actively wanted to create in my life. It also helped me to uncover that what is most important is uncovering why a fear exists in the first place, and the execution of dismantling that fear is what will free us from it. Learn to talk to it, ask what it needs, and understand how it manifested.

Do not take it on with distraction. And do not under any circumstances fake your way through it.

To unravel who you are without the fear, you must uncover the message it came to deliver.

One (of the many) coping skills I picked up over the years when faced with a fear is to overprepare, overanalyze, and overthink. This coping mechanism created a sense of control in my mind that could somehow distract from the feelings of anxiety. The choice to fixate on controlling situations, versus allowing room for flow, ease, and balance was my default.

I decided to book myself a hotel room by the airport, on the off chance I slept in as I would only be minutes from the airport. I also thought that the one-hour drive the night before into the city of Boston, followed by takeout and a bed away from home, would help to calm my nerves.

I went so far as to choose the exact three movies I would watch. A light romantic comedy before bed, to keep me laughing and calm, along with a comedy and a drama for the flight. A four-and-a-half-hour direct flight with two movies to cover the flight time. A good mix of laughter and emotion.

"Just keep yourself busy and you will not feel the anxiety." *Distraction.*

As it turned out, I so was nervous I did not sleep and could hardly eat any of the veggie pizza I ordered from room service. I had played that movie but could tell you the plot, the point, or the twist at the end. I got out of bed at 3:00 a.m. with a hotel room that smelled of onions from the pizza I never ate, got myself dressed, and headed to the lobby to take the shuttle bus to the airport.

As I settled into my seat, I looked around at the three passengers, sipping their coffee with heads down in their phones, possibly checking emails at this ungodly hour as if this were just another Wednesday morning routine. I got a glimpse of my reflection in the window and saw a tired, anxious version of myself and quickly looked away while reaching for my cell phone in my backpack.

When I arrived at the airport and settled into my gate, my adrenal system had kicked in so intensely it was as if I had been downing espressos for the last twenty-four hours. I made my way over to my seasoned traveling co-workers who appeared tired, yet very accustomed to this odd routine, like the strangers on the shuttle ride over. A very cheerful, high-pitched "good morning" blurted out.

Have you ever caught the sound of your own voice and recognized how rehearsed and fake it sounded when you're not speaking from a place of truth and alignment? Turns out that is a thing. A rise in our pitch when speaking is a common response to an anxious or nervous state. In that moment, I knew I was faking it.

If I had been honest in that moment it, I would have sounded more like, "Good morning. I have not slept, overpaid for a hotel room, am starving but too anxious to eat, and I accepted this position to overcome my irrational fear of flying which all seems very irrational now. How's your morning so far?"

Following my high-pitched greeting an announcement over the intercom said there was a one-hour delay because of the high winds which were causing the connecting flight to be delayed.

In that moment, my cool-as-a-cucumber coworker looked at me and said, "It's going to be a bumpy one. I love turbulence, it reminds me I'm alive."

If I were being honest my "yeah it's not so bad" response would have come out as "I think your brains have fallen out. We should start looking for them on the floor. It will be a great exercise in distraction for me. I also think this whole idea of deciding to accept this job that is going to have me on planes every other week is insane. My brains have fallen out too, so we are two women looking for our brains heading to Dallas at 5:00 a.m."

After my lie I immediately grabbed my phone to track the radar: cloudy overcast skies over most of New England, wind gusts up to forty miles per hour heading toward sunshine and warmer temperatures as we make our way toward Dallas. This weather check was preceded by going down a Facebook and Instagram rabbit hole, posting about my morning adventure with a smiley face to boot. I was not smiling on the inside.

As we boarded the flight, I made my way over to my seat, which I had selected when booking. Front of the plane, window seat. I may have had an intense fear of flying but I was not afraid of heights. By staring out into the clouds it was somehow comforting for me to be reminded of just how big this planet we live on is, and it made my problems, my worries, and my insecurities fade. The wanderlust in me loved those moments of quiet freedom.

I got situated in my seat and immediately put on my headphones and began to distract and tune out. That stress response that was happening in my body was a message asking me to tune in. I diverted and chose distraction.

I remember the plane taking off and closing my eyes so tightly I may have even forgot to breathe. I did manage to peek out of the window and see a spectacular sunrise over the clouds and for a moment that calm tried lovingly to make its way into my thoughts as hidden messages will do, just before my brain would take over telling me that I was in danger. Once we were in flight, I started my plan. Begin the first movie: that will get you through the first half of the flight. Before you know it, we will be on the ground.

Then the turbulence began, and all bets were off for my enjoying this flight. I gripped the armrest and closed my eyes. Just then I felt a hand on mine. I opened my eyes to find that the older gentleman in the middle seat next to me was attempting to . . . hold my hand.

I have always prided myself on being a kind and patient human, and my empathetic heart recognizes the goodness in others within minutes of meeting them. Call it instinct, call it a gut knowing. I say it's being human. In that moment with the plane bobbing up and down, flight attendants now halting all beverage services until this nonsense was over, I grabbed this man's hand back, and there I was thirty-three thousand feet in the air at 7:00 a.m. on a Wednesday, holding hands with a stranger.

As it turns out, this stranger was a retired pilot who was traveling to visit his daughter in Dallas. He had also recognized my obvious discomfort for air travel and soon we went from holding hands to discussing all the ins and outs of flying. He went into detail of how the planes work, of what certain sounds were in the cabin and around the plane. He made me laugh and get teary-eyed when he spoke about his family. He talked to me as a dad would talk to their daughter who was sitting in fear. And then he said something I will never forget.

"Are you afraid of flying or are you afraid of the unknown?"

The aha moment. The unknown.

There was evidence all throughout my life in which fear-based thought patterns kept me from fully living. In that moment, a memory flooded into my mind, and I could not help but pause and recount the ways I had let fear take over.

My parents had my brother convert our old home movies into a DVD. I have always felt it is an odd and fascinating thing to watch yourself as a child, to take a step back into a time you have no recollection of and yet there you are learning to crawl. In one of the videos, I'm about seven years old. We're on a summer vacation in New Hampshire on what appears to be a jungle gym. It had a tunnel made of white netting that led to another enclosed tunnel, and there I am awkwardly walking through the net toward the tunnel when suddenly I stop. I'm staring down that tunnel as if to say, "If I take one step closer it's going to swallow me whole." With the conviction a person being chased by a bear I turn around and high tailed it out of there. The unknown is staring me in the face.

I enjoyed the rest of that flight and realized this was the distraction I needed. It was not tuning out with a movie or social media. The key to unlocking these destructive sequences of my body's reaction to fear-based thoughts was found in becoming more emotionally open and receptive to finding safety in open-hearted conversation. In connection, sharing, honesty, openness, and vulnerability.

To move past my fear, I had to tune in to the messages around me and ask better questions. What was this fear trying to tell me? Then, when I began the work of understanding the fear, it was time to dismantle.

As time went on my fear of flying faded away. It became more than just overcoming a fear of flying, it created a path toward uncovering a deep-rooted core belief that I was in danger and fearing the unknown, not trusting myself and allowing anxiety to overtake my life. With each flight, I began to look forward to those quiet moments in flight moving through the clouds and catching the sunrise and sunsets fill up the sky with the most spectacular shows. I eased into my plans leading up to my travels and found myself chatting with strangers. I created rituals such as calming meditation music during takeoff and journaling about my feelings the night before a trip, versus distracted coping mechanisms to ease any anxious feelings.

By learning to let go and allow, I gained confidence, humility, grace, and forgiveness. This opened the door to more travel, something I actively wanted to call into my life.

WHERE IS FEAR SHOWING UP IN YOUR MIND?

Take a minute to think of something that creates a fear-based thought pattern in your mind. I invite you to explore any areas in your life in which you feel fear is creating worry, anxiety, or obsessive thought patterns. Take the time to step into those fears with an open mind and the willingness to be open to the possibility of finding something beautiful beyond their grasp.

As an example, it could be the fear of losing your job or the business you love. Instead of focusing on that fear, reframe it and think of what you appreciate about your work, and even all that is good in your life. You can do this practice out loud or write these examples down. Do this exercise as often as you need to. There is no right or wrong way. The important piece is that you begin to understand that fear at times is asking us to believe in something we cannot see. However, faith requires us to do the same. We get to decide which one to lean into to create lasting change.

Building a relationship to self, I would begin to learn, is a slow and gradual process of reconnecting to our mind and body. It's understanding how to witness our fears without judgment and instead lean into them with curiosity and compassion.

A SPACE FOR JOURNALING AND REFLECTION.

A SPACE FOR JOURNALING AND REFLECTION.

CHAPTER 2

"Someone I loved once gave me a box full of darkness. It took me years to understand that this too, was a gift."

MARY OLIVER

I was twenty-four at the time, young, vulnerable, and just beginning to learn how to navigate through the emotional trials of unhealthy love. I was standing at the entrance to my apartment, crouched on the ground in tears. I did not want to go into my own home. This was beginning to become a regular occurrence. On the other side of the door was someone I cared about deeply, but mistakenly viewed their consistent control and passive emotional availability as love. The more they leaned away, the more I leaned in.

This was the moment, however, crouched on the ground, that I finally freed myself from emotional abuse.

My commute home from work was at least an hour from Boston to Providence and I cherished that alone time in my car. As I approached my apartment my body would begin to tighten, and I could feel the tension rise into my throat. I felt powerless and fragile.

I reached into my bag and frantically searched for my cell phone and called a friend.

"This isn't where I'm supposed to be," I whispered into the phone in between tears.

"Then go," she replied, with enough conviction and truth in her voice to allow me a moment of strength and clarity to go. In the moments when you want the ground to open and swallow you whole, there are the friends who grab onto your hand and hold space for you, maybe just through the voice at the other end of a phone. Those friends—keep them close.

I had put most of my friends and family in a position in which I wanted them to listen to the pain of this relationship yet support the love that I held in my heart for this person, asking them to ride along on this rollercoaster of emotional dysfunction.

I was young when we met, only twenty-two. I was out with friends and remember seeing him from across the room. It was as if the blaring music in the nightclub and the echoes of voices suddenly stopped when he looked in my direction and walked toward me. I know that sounds like I am pulling it out of some scene in a romantic comedy but it's how my mind remembers when we first met. He was charming, cultured, and charismatic. I was lost, unsure, and lacked confidence. The perfect match for someone who craved control and for someone like me who did not yet understand that control will never mean love.

We would spend most weekends out dancing, partying, and usually only with his friends. Our life together was clouded with those late weekend nights and my being home alone most weeknights distracting myself with television and shopping. His lack of presence and lack of communication as to where he was or what time I would expect him to return home was growing evidence I was not standing in my power or being held in a partnership in which healthy communication and transparency were present.

The emotional abuse in this relationship was gradual. In the beginning there were moments of fun, laughter, and what I mistakenly viewed as support. There were promises made in the beginning that we would be happy together, that our life would be filled with travel and adventure. My young heart danced in delight at the thought of a life filled with fun and distraction. I did not realize the abuse existed until I was fully entangled in its web, until I felt powerless over it and unable to properly stand in my power. It had become an internal prison where I was seeking to be loved and chosen at any cost.

Wanting desperately to be with this person as much as possible I quickly moved in with them without a thought, without asking myself if it was what I wanted. And slowly I began to have no voice in our home. It began with no say in our finances, what was for dinner, or how our home was decorated. I have always felt strongly that the spaces we live in are connected to the way that we feel so this disconnect that occurred in my home made me feel lost and uninspired.

My feelings began to become discredited, unheard, and not up for discussion. His views on the world had to become mine or I was called disloyal and jaded. I felt parts of myself slowly fall away as I was made to feel that I could not do anything right. From the clothes I wore, to the way I spoke to others, I was under a constant microscope of judgement and control.

This form of psychological invalidation is one of the most lethal forms of emotional abuse. It can hurt confidence, creativity, and individuality. It shatters self-esteem and this loss of oneself can perpetuate the decision of staying in a relationship out of the pure fear of leaving.

In my naive mind I had felt that abuse was only physical. Not words, not silencing me, or manipulation of my feelings. Not complete control. I thought there had to be visible bruises or physical evidence. Not insides filled with pain.

I never would have wanted violence but that abuse would have been easier to recognize.

I stayed because I wanted to display my independence of being young and not having to live with my parents but these reasons were excuses as I fell prey to the common cycle of abuse.

Two years into the relationship we took a trip overseas. To most of my friends and family it seemed exciting that I was going to be adventuring off to different countries, taking time out of my life to do some wandering and exploring. There was a part of me that craved the freedom in this opportunity, and I also felt it could somehow bring us closer. This was the first time I was leaving the country, and about one month before the trip, I started experiencing health issues.

I was getting headaches, fatigue, and frequent stomachaches. I chalked it up to how much I was working and lack of sleep. I was telling myself and others how excited I was to be traveling to some of the most beautiful European countries and how our itinerary was filled with so many incredible adventures. I felt an emptiness inside of me as I thought about sharing these moments with the person who was the object of my growing anger and resentment. Leaning on any glimmer of hope that we would enjoy this time together, my insides were screaming "no," yet I continued responding with a "yes."

When we arrived on the first leg of our trip I was exhausted from the flight and began to feel sick as the jet lag took over. I was only interested in sleeping. As I walked into his family's home I was told to "wake up and help with whatever was needed." There was no compassion or understanding and I spent most of our time on that trip very unwell, hiding behind a fake smile as I tried desperately to take in the beauty of each day's adventures. The state of my health was dismissed and ignored, and I was told I was "seeking attention."

In retrospect, my body was, in fact, seeking attention. It wanted me to know it was tired of my continually not choosing myself, of neglecting my own worth and not putting myself in a safe space to grow, heal, and evolve—all messages from my nervous system. Symptoms were the only relief my body could seem to find from carrying around all this pain. The hurt, the fear, the rejection. The hiding, the depriving, the self-abandoning.

When you finally learn that a person's behavior has more to do with their own internal struggle that it ever did with you, you learn grace.

CHOOSING ME

The day I left I walked into the house and headed for the bedroom. I opened the closet and clumsily looked for my suitcase. In a shaking voice I found the courage to say, "I think it is time for me to go," as I began packing up my clothing in that home that never felt like my own. As I emptied out the drawers and the closet I kept my head down and felt nothing. I wasn't moved to cry, scream, or even speak. For the first time in my life, I was emotionless. I felt nothing.

There was bewilderment and confusion coming out of his mouth, but I never explained why I was leaving. I kept my head down and kept packing. His voice was blurry in the background. I could not make out his words, I could only feel the energy in the room, which was heavy and uncomfortable. A true testament to the years I had spent with this person.

I do not remember all the details of my leaving. There are parts of my mind that have chosen to place this part of my life in a box that was not meant to be opened. But I do know I got in my car and drove to my parents without looking back.

This could be the part of the story when you are cheering me on and routing for me. When you are so incredibly happy I broke away. Maybe you are picturing me riding off into the sunset toward my healing and better days: windows down, music loud, wind flying through the car. Maybe you have experienced the same type of abuse or are intertwined in it and looking for hope to move on.

You can and you will. But my story did not quite go this way just yet.

It seems that we sometimes know perfectly well how to birth the pain and fuel the storms inside of us but have no idea what to do with all the love that lives there. Especially, most importantly, the love we have for ourselves.

When I left this relationship, I quickly moved myself into another without the time to heal, reflect, or process. I did not allow myself space to breathe or give my body the rest it needed after living in a state of hypervigilance for so long. I repeated the patterns of distraction and desperately searched for love.

I found new love, and this time fell into patterns of codependency in which I found it hard to communicate my feelings, valuing the approval of this person more so than myself. I was making sacrifices to ensure they were happy, until the years went by and I became completely empty and began to shut them out. I wanted so badly to create the perfect picture of what I felt was a happy and secure love. But I lost sight of the most important relationship we can ever have and that is the one with ourselves.

I believe we must be brave enough to heal ourselves even when it hurts. I believe that if the pain of staying in our patterns of self-betrayal are more painful than remaining in our current circumstance, we must choose to dive inward.

"Never be afraid to dive inward,
your soul will catch you."

The next relationship lasted over a decade, and in its ending my insides began letting me know it was time to finally heal the relationship I had with myself. To move toward myself and try to rebuild on my own, not carrying another into my own wounds but allowing them to be free. There are times we can rebuild our hearts together and there are times we do this work on our own.

By this time in my life I was forty and felt as though there was something terribly wrong with me for inflicting my pain onto another, for never following my urges for freedom and self-reflection, and for never truly allowing myself to experience a life unattached.

I was forty and had been in a string of relationships since I was sixteen.

Being single for the first time in over two decades felt like the scariest yet most exciting place I had ever been. Where these lessons and heartache took me was a small dark room where I had to sit with my feelings and take personal responsibility for why I had never crafted a healthy and loving relationship with myself but rather continually choose others to define my worth and purpose.

This was one of the hardest things to face and uncover. And I did not walk through this alone.

I believe it is okay to ask for help, guidance, and support when we are moving through a healing journey. I called on my closest friends, found a wonderful therapist, and was very gentle and compassionate with myself.

I fell in love with living alone, being single (with purpose) and enjoying my own company.

I created a morning and nightly routine of journaling and allowed myself to free write around my feelings which became one of the most therapeutic things I could do.

Asking yourself to uncover why you made choices that moved you further and further away from your true self takes more than a night out with a friend, a glass of red wine, and discussing over dinner. Looking yourself in the mirror, rather than pointing the finger at the person who caused the pain and saying, "I made this choice to stay. I decided in those moments this person was worth more than my worth" is where the healing starts.

It is hard work, the hardest work. If the pain of making these choices has finally become the loudest bully in the room, then it is time to stand up to that bully and lean into yourself. The fear of leaving cannot be stronger than the wanting to go.

It seems sometimes we are the ones who have broken our own hearts.

SELF-LOVE NOTES FOR MOVING THROUGH HEARTBREAK

Living in an illusion of what could be will never allow us to fully expand. It keeps us stuck in the possibility rather than taking responsibility for what we are choosing.

Internalizing behaviors and becoming fixated on fixing others creates a separation of self. That separation does not allow for our growth.

The critical inner voice that plays within our minds that says "I am not enough" when others have hurt us can be witnessed and tended to. By practicing awareness when it comes up, we can lovingly stop judging ourselves and change the narrative to promote self-love and healing.

Avoidance and distraction when we are going through the loss of a partnership can at times prevent us from doing the work needed to move toward ourselves. Moving toward self will in turn provide us with a strong foundation for a healthy relationship.

Repressing our emotions does not mean they leave us. Allowing the pain, but not becoming it, is important. Witnessing it without judgement and allowing it to be there creates a safe space in our body for the pain to move through us.

Loving relationships are fundamental to living a thriving life. Whether they are the relationship we hold with a parent, a friend, or our romantic partners, they help us to grow as individuals, are wonderful for our health and nervous system as they lack chronic stress on the body, and most importantly they reflect how we see ourselves.

You will never regret building the one most precious relationship you have with yourself. It will define all others.

A SPACE FOR JOURNALING AND REFLECTION.

A SPACE FOR JOURNALING AND REFLECTION.

CHAPTER 3

"Maybe we are searching among the branches for what only appears in the roots."

RUMI

Since I was a child, I have been what society proclaims a daydreamer. I honor that title and cherish it. It is one of the most complimentary things someone could say about a person.

What are you truly if you aren't in a state of dreaming at some points throughout the day? To dream while awake is one of the most honest things you can do. To become intertwined among the stars at night and dream can be magical, but to land in your dreams in the daylight hours and revel in possibility and ideas that play out your soul's deepest truth is an act of courage.

To dream sparks curiosity. And curiosity followed long enough will lead to discovering new paths.

Where have you stopped becoming curious in your life? If there is a question burning inside of you that must be answered, follow it. Curiosity followed long enough will eventually land you where you are meant to be. And where exactly is that? Living out your most authentic truth. Diving deep into a life where your insides match your outsides.

I have learned the road map to find our authentic truth is not linear. It seems the more jagged the path, the more forks in the road that appear, the more likely we are to eventually find our place: our place of authenticity, truth, and an inner knowing only we understand.

The place where dreams are made.

I have become so intently curious throughout my life as to why a traditional way of living was never a path I felt drawn to. I rejected the idea of having children and settling into a forever home. As a child, when I thought of the future version of myself, she wasn't sashaying down the aisle to meet her prince charming in a white dress. She was wondering what it would be like to live on the moon or to wander around Paris eating croissants. However, I still had deep-rooted beliefs and ideals centered around the importance of family and tradition. The delicate dance I would play out between the always-present feeling that there was something else just outside of my grasp challenged my feelings on the traditional. There were layers inside of me always wondering, curious, and alive with possibility. Always chasing.

There was a span of two decades of my life when I completely lost track of who I was. I don't regret that time. Acceptance is a long, dark road filled with shame and guilt that you must endure and face to come to a place of deep compassion for yourself. I have to come to know that this lost time in my life happened because I stopped being curious. I stopped asking questions to move myself forward. I stopped listening to that inner guidance system moving toward my most authentic self.

I am not convinced there was a particular moment I stopped living authentically that began this journey toward loss of self, but rather it transpired over time. I suppose it may have begun over the course of a few years when I slowly stopped seeking out my own interests and became fixated on fitting into the mold of others: working a nine-to-five when I preferred flexibility in my days, getting married by a certain age rather than ensuring my partner and I were a good fit, choosing to follow a path of certainty versus exploration.

As this path unfolded and I moved away from what my heart truly wanted for my life, it soon became a road I could not turn back from. A road I lost myself on. Each time I moved away from what felt true to me, I built momentum in a direction that eventually led to heartbreak, poor decisions, illness, and the profound loss of self: the jobs I took that I knew I wouldn't enjoy and the friendships built on wanting to fit in rather than just being myself. I have come to know that saying "yes" when our insides are screaming "no" is one of the greatest losses of self we will encounter in our lives.

Was it intentional? No. But lying to ourselves about who we are, what lights us up, what our soul needs to feel loved, comforted, inspired, and understood is dangerous ground. I've had to reach into the deepest parts of myself to find compassion for this idea that my true being was, in fact, enough.

At times, on our path to unraveling our choices and even our calling, we circle back to our roots. To what molded us and shaped our path. Having always been curious about my family background and wanting to further understand my lineage, I was fortunate enough to uncover details about my family's past that allowed me insight into uncovering my own unique personality traits. Our ancestral experience guides and informs the familial and personal story line in ways that can help us understand our lives as well as our conditioning.

My parents were born from the post-World War II baby boom. Their parents descended from western Europe, Italy, and Portugal. My father's side of the family has a history deeply rooted in the arts.

The gestation of the Giammarco family came from Sulmona, Italy. Sulmona is in the Italian region of Abruzzo in the province of L'Aquila, about one hundred miles north of Rome.

My great-great-grandfather Salvatore Giammarco was a painter and master horseman. He and his wife, Maddalena, owned a small tavern in the town. Salvatore was a follower of Carlo Tresca, a prominent anarchist who was an opponent of fascism, communism, and the Mafia's influence on the Italian trade unions. Salvatore held clandestine meetings in the tavern with other Tresca supporters. As such, he was a target of the local authorities for his political views and ultimately moved to Argentina. While in Argentina, he was severely injured in a horse accident and died of an infection. His oldest son emigrated to the United States in 1904 at the age of eighteen. Maddalena and the other children followed over the next three years. All arrived via Boston.

A consistent trait of the Giammarcos that touches every generation of the family is art, music, and strong individualism. Even today, many of the family members who reside in Italy and other parts of the world continue to paint and sculpt professionally. Many members of the family also are musicians. When my great-grandfather first arrived in America, he and his brothers, not able to support themselves as artists, found work as painters, carpenters, and ceramic tile installers. However, they continued to paint and sculpt. My great-grandfather Cesare and his oldest brother Gaetano were commissioned to paint religious murals and sculpt statues for the local Catholic churches, some of which still exist today. Their homes were like museums with scenes of their native Sulmona painted on walls and small sculptures located in every room.

Artists are dreamers who found the courage to go against the status quo.

Once my family settled into America, my parent's fathers fought wars and their mothers worked hard in factories. They did everything for their families. I lucked out with this strong example of support. I understand and live in full awareness of this privilege. Their display of love is rooted in doing and helping and in a boots-on-the-ground, let's-get-to-work attitude. My parents are traditional, supportive, and responsible. They went off to college, fell in love, got married, provided for their family, and over the course of almost fifty years, have not ceased in this life decision. My extended family has followed the same traditional path, and to this day family is one of the most important values in my life. Our family gatherings are still rooted in music and in self-expression, which is inherently in our genes.

Yet there is a strong crossover into the traditional and practical. The path of life that follows full self-expression became intertwined with a life that followed a more traditional path.

My parents' choices were practical, smart, and calculated, and they understood sacrifice. You worked hard for your family; you showed your love by doing. By showing up.

They seemed to lay out this path of knowing do effortlessly. Raising children, creating a home. My mom stayed home to raise us while my dad worked.

Our home was always in order. Clean sheets weekly on the beds, organized linen closets, not a speck of dust to be seen. Meals were ready on the table for dinner by 6:00 p.m., and somehow my mom managed to juggle the busy social and activity calendars of three children while still managing to keep our home perfectly in order. My dad would travel to Asia and Europe for business, coming home to talk all about his travels. Old photos of family trips to Disney World and Lake George fill up our photo albums. We were the picture of a happy family living well in America.

Yet this more traditional path was not mine to follow. As I spent hours in my room writing poetry, journaling, and gazing out the window in awe of this planet, I was always curious, wondering. Always wanting to reach out of the crafted life with one hand always firmly holding onto the comfort found in the four walls of my room.

It is clear that emotional maturity does not peak at the age of eighteen, but being the deep feeling gal I am, feelings tend to overtake me. I, like most teens, struggled with fitting in, wanting desperately to be seen and appear as everyone else.

I experienced moments of anxiety, worry, and confusion that created such a shift in focus from getting to know myself and who I was becoming in the world to complete misalignment with my place in the world. I didn't know how to make choices in service of me, and the thought of having to decide on a career or life path terrified me. As I witnessed friends going off to college and choosing a career path, the voice of comparison began to speak. I confused other people's choices and opportunities as false evidence of something being terribly wrong within myself. A story of unworthiness began to play so loudly in my thinking mind that I did what I knew best. Divert, distract, and bury away the messages that this feeling of unworthiness was trying to tell me. The message that living unauthentically was going to throw me off course.

I would sacrifice my time, my well-being, and my values just to fit in. It was almost as if fitting in meant choosing a different version of myself over and over.

I allowed the fear of being my true self to overtake my life. Like the little girl holding onto the safety and comfort of home, I was fearfully gripping the false version of myself.

Fear lies in knowing our true selves, because that often means change, loss, discomfort, and everything we've been afraid to let go of. I chose to stay in the comfort and bury away the authentic parts of myself that needed to grow.

This loss of self leaked into every area of my life. Distraction looked like studying hard in my college courses and changing majors five times before landing on one that held no interest in who I am as an individual, but rather one that would allow me to appear as though I was smart and making a practical choice: business management. My family dubbed me "the perpetual student." My career choices being misaligned created stress, fatigue, frequent sickness, and ongoing anxiety.

I fell into relationships with men whom I had no deep connection to out of fear of being alone. I began living out inaccurate beliefs about who I was, and I abandoned the parts of myself that needed the most attention.

By my midtwenties, my retail career consisted of floating in and out jobs, no clear direction, and seeking happiness outside of myself. In retrospect, I was living in a state of misalignment. To distract myself from feeling unhappy with my choices and lacking direction, my weekends were filled with nightclubs, drinking, and then heading into work on less than three hours of sleep. I lived for the weekends so I could distract and remain numb. It was what I call a by-me life. A life that is consumed within our own minds, without awareness of our actions, choices, or personal responsibility for our lives. My way or the highway. Confusion, chaos, reacting. In lust with life versus in love with it.

And my body knew. It always knew. This was the time in my life it began to scream loudly, and I repeatedly used distraction and covered my eyes and ears to the messages. Self-betrayal and denying parts of ourselves in order to be loved not for who we are, but versions others approve of, proved itself to be one of the greatest lessons in authenticity.

When I found myself again, I was able to understand that protecting myself for fear of being seen as I am was only holding me back.

I encourage you to explore this area of your life with an open mindset and curiosity. You can choose to change your story, break ancestral patterns, or use the information simply as a doorway into a past that allows you a greater love and compassion for your ancestors and provides a greater understanding of who you are by bringing history to life.

Here are the things I have learned on my journey back to me that can help you create a truthful inner guidance system that remains at the forefront of your decision-making and helps to guide you back home to yourself.

PRACTICAL STEPS TO YOUR TRUTH

Ask yourself what happened just before you made one of the best choices in your life.

Take the time to do some digging here and think about a choice you made that you knew was in complete service of you. That choice that brought you joy, elation, excitement, and full-body chills. That choice you knew was one of the best decisions in your life. Maybe it was the relationship you took a chance on based on a true feeling of connection, the job you took despite the fear, or waking up and deciding to spend the day wandering in nature.

Just before you made those choices that brought you to a place of inner peace, happiness, and alignment, what was your thought process? Most likely your insides were screaming, "Yes, more of this!" You were expanding versus shrinking. Follow those prompts and use those to lead you to making choices that light you up.

Do not try to fit in. Notice when you are trying hard to.

Trying to fit in doesn't work. Being yourself works for you, which is honestly the most important relationship in your life. Moving on from people, jobs, situations that don't fit into the mold that you wish to create for yourself is not abandonment, it is a declaration of self-love.

Whenever I stayed in a job or relationship in which I did not feel safe or supported in being my true self, I would find myself overcompensating and people-pleasing. This is like waving your own red flag of inauthentic behavior. You want to be waving those green flags that give yourself the opportunity to go and be you.

Pay attention to what you do in your down time that feeds your soul.

Are there any hobbies you enjoy doing that immediately calm your insides and make you feel alive? It could be painting, writing, or even watching *Jeopardy!*. The point is there are hidden clues in these activities that give us some insight into what our soul truly loves. And our soul really loves it when we live from that place.

I have been in love with decorating and crafting spaces for as long as I can remember. When I was eight, I even wrote in my journal that I was going to grow up to be a closet organizer. When I was in my midthirties and r-evaluating my life, I started a part-time organizing business. It was one of the best choices I had ever made and led to meeting incredible clients, television appearances, and writing opportunities. I followed a passion. It doesn't need to become a business venture for you, but it can provide a path to self-discovery and lead you back to yourself.

Remember, you are not here to fulfill roles other people have crafted for you. You are here to live in your own unique purpose. When we don't use our energy toward the truest, realest version of ourselves, we are denying parts of ourselves meant to be explored, experienced, and lived.

It can be painful to uncover why you are here, but each time you take a step toward yourself, you are breaking free.

A SPACE FOR JOURNALING AND REFLECTION.

A SPACE FOR JOURNALING AND REFLECTION.

CHAPTER 4

"Not all storms come to disrupt your life. Some come to clear your path."

UNKNOWN

It was Christmas morning, but it felt different this time.

I woke up with my head slightly buzzing from the prior evening's traditional Christmas Eve gathering with my family. For close to four decades, my extended family would gather together on Christmas Eve. It was a tradition everyone would be present for and an opportunity to reconnect and celebrate.

This year, waking up on Christmas morning, my body was aching and exhausted. This feeling had been with me for weeks but still felt incredibly foreign. Almost as if I were somehow inside someone else's body. It could not have been mine. I lay there for a moment with my eyes tightly closed hoping I would miraculously return to ***my*** body. The one I recognized as my own.

Just two months prior, these legs had walked me up mountains that were over four thousand feet high. They had moved without effort in dance class. They had carried me on over forty hikes in the last twelve months. *How could they suddenly be aching at just the simple task of walking?*

In years past, Christmas morning looked like caffeinating, hustling out the door to visit family, and piling gifts into the car as we indulged in all the holiday season has to offer. After staring blankly at my tired eyes in the bathroom mirror, I got dressed and gathered up my luggage. It had been packed for two days. My dad drove me to the airport, and we hugged goodbye. While my backpack and sneakers moved through airport security and I walked toward my departure gate, I realized that for the first time in forty-one years, I would be alone on Christmas.

In that moment I felt a weight lifting and, paradoxically, my heart sinking. The clarity around this decision to be spending Christmas alone and the imbalance of emotions because of my mysterious condition seemed to create confusion and overwhelm. I was committed to becoming whole by myself but did not recognize who I was.

I landed in the far northwestern tip of Florida, otherwise known as the Panhandle, on Christmas Day. I had googled "the best beaches nobody goes to" when deciding where to stay. I picked the right location.

I had booked this trip in the days prior to my symptoms. At that time, the thought of solo travel headed to sunshine on a beach in Florida followed by a road trip from San Francisco to Los Angeles seemed like magic. After the emotional roller coaster of divorce, I was ready for an escape. Now I was wondering how I was going to manage making it through the flight.

I have always known that the mind and body connection is strong. Was the transition into this new life of being on my own so intensely met with emotion that my body was breaking down? Was this why my body suddenly seemed to be failing me?

As I drove closer to my destination, the stretch of highway slowly became a beautiful and wild stretch of road surrounded by water on either side. I had the windows down to feel the breeze. The air was warm and dry, and the sun felt like gold on my face that had been used to the cold New England air.

As I headed toward the condo I had rented for a few days, on the beach nestled between a pier and the surrounding vacation homes, I felt a sense of calm wash over me. I became distracted by the welcome change of scenery. This seasonal beach town was quiet and empty, with only locals filling the homes that lined the coast. When I arrived, I opened the sliding doors to find the ocean almost at my feet, lit up with most incredibly sunset. I sat my luggage down, pulled up a chair, and found myself staring out into the ocean for what seemed like hours. I watched the sky fade from the most brilliant colors of red and orange to blues and purples before it became lit up with stars. I climbed into bed and prayed that somehow this magical place would cure my insides and I would awaken feeling refreshed and vibrant.

My last night in Florida my body was gently asking me to return home. My fatigue was so intense it felt like an effort to even speak. But I chose to ignore the signals of exhaustion and pain. I got myself out of bed for an early flight to San Francisco, where my cousin was picking me up. The wanderlust in me was too excited for our road trip adventure from Northern California to Los Angeles. We had live music planned for each night and friends to visit on our journey. I continued to live in denial that my insides were asking me to please rest or understand the emotion trapped within my body that was asking to be seen and heard.

I tried my hardest to be present on the trip. To take in the beauty of the landscape that was surrounding me. To stay awake to the music, laughter, and new experiences—all environments that I would otherwise thrive in. But my body was rejecting my soul's willingness to feel free.

Our travels took us southeast from San Francisco to Los Angeles. The scenery slowly changed from lush greens to miles of farmland and desert terrain. Always changing, always beautiful. Smiling faces and amazing people inviting me into their homes and evenings filled with live music. Yet all I wanted to do was sleep.

During a show at the Orpheum Theatre in San Francisco, too exhausted to stand, I found a seat in the back of the theatre and actually took a nap during the show. What was happening in my body was in sharp contrast to this incredible environment I had planned for myself.

My trip ended on New Year's Eve. It was cut short the day before by the most intense brain fog and body aches I had ever felt. I slept for close to fourteen hours and then on New Year's Eve headed home. The moment the plane took off from Los Angeles to head across the country, despite my aching joints and the feeling I had the worst flu that never seemed to end, I drifted off into a deep sleep. I awoke in time to catch the sun, setting on a decade. A decade that left me feeling lost, emotionally spent, and feeling defeated.

The state of my body and mind seemed to erase any concern for appearing as an emotional wreck, as I let the tears fall without effort. I cried for the life I was leaving behind, and I cried most for not understanding why I felt so incredibly ill for so long.

When I finally arrived at home, I collapsed on my bed, too weak to even welcome the idea of celebrating the new year. Sleep began to be my reprieve from the dizziness, the physical pain, and the unrelenting fatigue. My routine began to resemble something out of a nightmare. I would get out of bed and scan my body, focusing on every pain point and what was wrong. I would then get into the shower and have to sit to be able to properly wash my hair, as I was too exhausted to stand. I would also skip breakfast, too nauseous to eat or even think about food. And then I would drive my weak, aching body into work. I would sit there for hours doing my work, fixated on googling all my symptoms. Then I would head home to immediately put on my pajamas, crawl into bed, and try to sleep, only to wake up and do it all over the next day. It was torture. I was missing the point of what my body was asking me to pay attention to until a walk led me to uncover what needed to happen next.

About a month into this continuous cycle, I somehow found the strength to take a drive with a friend to one of my favorite hiking spots in Rhode Island, Trustom Pond National Wildlife Refuge.

Patsy is the kind of friend every woman needs in her life. She listens intently without judgment, without injecting her own story to relate. She just shows up ready to be a friend. When I called and asked her to meet me for a walk, she did not hesitate.

It was a mild winter that year, two months before the world would land in the pandemic. The trail started with rounding a marsh and then would walk you through a magical wooden trail. Known for its birdlife, it was a place I would travel to often looking for a blue jay or a cardinal. The end of the trail rounded a corner, where you found yourself walking up a wooden deck to the most beautiful views of the Atlantic. This trail reminded me of how incredibly blessed I had been to live in a state surrounded by over two hundred miles of coastline.

As we made our way to the deck and took a seat, I started opening up about how I felt in my body. How I did not recognize myself. How when I looked in the mirror, I saw a scared person, who was dropping weight faster than was healthy for my body.

"I'm not eating. I cannot sleep. I'm in pain, I'm scared."

"What do you think is the worst that can happen?"

That was not the first time I had been asked that question, but it was the first time I wanted to answer with the word "death." And that was scary.

"That it's going to swallow me whole."

"But what about an outcome of the highest good?"

The highest good. I let that sink in. *What was on the other side of this?*

As walked back to the car, my eyes fell on the most beautiful tree.

I suppose I am a tree hugger in the sense that I appreciate how long they have been standing tall on this earth. Providing us with oxygen, giving us life, asking for nothing in return. Most trees can withstand every season, regardless of the weather that circles around them. Their roots are deeply planted into the ground, with branches able to bend before breaking. And they keep growing.

"As above, so below."

The words left my lips before I could even think of what I was going to say.

If you aren't familiar with the meaning behind these words, they are a spiritual reference that implies that whatever happens in nature is reflected within the human body. It dates back to Hermes, a god in Greek mythology.

Patsy looked over at me and smiled. I knew instinctively in that moment it was all connected. The human body is connected to the larger universe. There is a piece missing in my illness that I am not seeing. I believe in that moment my true healing journey began.

Two months later, I would receive my medical diagnosis of chronic fatigue syndrome and fibromyalgia, otherwise known as CFS/ME. This came after multiple diagnostic tests, lab work, doctor appointments, second opinions, hearing, "All of your test results are normal" after five months of facing these symptoms without answers, and ultimately after doing extensive research myself and presenting these facts to my doctors.

I did not, however, allow my diagnosis to become my identity. I simply saw the explanation as the medical terminology to describe the symptoms. I did not become fixated on the diagnosis and the belief that it was a lifelong sentence.

When I stopped becoming a victim to my past, my circumstances, and my inability to voice my truth, I began to take ownership of my life. I understood that healing my body meant understanding I am worthy of living a life in full alignment of me.

This happened in multiple stages. Conscious awareness was the first step: realistically understanding that something needed to change. This was followed by personal responsibility. I would declare daily to myself, "I am the only one responsible for my healing." Whether others understood my unique new path I was creating did not have any bearing on whether I would begin to heal.

As someone who had always felt responsible for the emotions of others, this was difficult to navigate. But practicing this daily mantra created a new level of confidence within me I did not realize I had. Despite how sick I may have been, it provided me with a sense of self for the first time in my life. It is easier to let go of the opinions of others when we fully understand that others are simply seeing us through their past or their current emotion.

The personal responsibility phase was one of the most interesting places to land. Suddenly I had to find the strength to forgive myself for not honoring my own needs for so long and placing my worth in the hands of others. Holding no judgement for myself and finding compassion for the ways I had acted in the past was a crucial part of healing. Releasing that burden felt like one of the most freeing things I could do, and I offered myself the opportunity to move forward.

I eased into the normalcy of an entirely different lifestyle and full acceptance of my condition. I slowed my body down, began working from home, and adjusted my life seeing this as a call to action from my insides that something needed to be tended to.

CFS/ME can present itself in two ways: postviral infection in the body or an active one. Or, as in the case with myself, after emotional trauma or improperly dealing with stressors. It is also common among those who tend to be overachievers and perfectionists. It is essentially a neuroimmune illness that causes the nervous system to misfire, which affects the body as a whole.

In Kenneth J. Friedman's article "Advances in ME/CFS: Past, Present, and Future," he cited a 2015 Institute of Medicine report on the illness that declared ME/CFS affects an estimated 2.5 million people. Most cases go undiagnosed. As with any illness or disease, both physical and mental, you cannot speak to its depths unless you are in the throes of it.

The path to recovery is a delicate balance of putting the puzzle pieces together with proper nutrition, appropriate rest, restorative movement, emotional work, and faith.

Making the decision to seek out support and gain the tools needed to return my body to a natural balanced state was one of the best choices I made on my healing path. It became the turning point for me to accept what was happening to my body and begin to understand that living in a new way was going to be a true catalyst to my healing. As my story unfolds throughout the book, I will dive deep into the core habit changes I adopted and still carry out daily that sustain wellness throughout my body and mind. I credit the start of this healing journey to CFS Health and the team it has in place for support.

When you are committed to healing, accepting you cannot move forward without living in a new way is at the core of wellness. Yet it is so easily avoided as our body loves for us to remain on autopilot. It's truly a safety net for our nervous system.

There are a few revelations that I have come to know along this journey. Understanding why we refuse to stand firm in boundaries, navigate away from our true selves, and avoid staring down our pain does not look perfectly placed and joyful. It's not a highlight reel for social media. It is messy and hard and maybe even bizarre to some. But it represents the raw truth of unbecoming and stepping into who we were meant to be.

> *"Maybe the journey isn't so much about becoming anything. Maybe it's about un-becoming everything that really isn't you, so you can be who you were meant to be in the first place."*
>
> PAULO COELHO

THE POWER OF THE MIND-BODY CONNECTION

To find the most authentic version of me meant slowly releasing so much, in the physical and nonphysical. Some of what to release was understood, such as accepting where I was in this chapter of my life, and rather than focusing on my limitations, deciding to face them. Any belief system I had picked up as truth, in relation to our thought process and unease settling into our bodies, was confirmed.

Over the years, the mind and body connection and how it relates to our health has become increasingly talked about. Metaphysical counselor, teacher, and healer Louise Hay authored a book called *You Can Heal Your Life*. She explains how our thoughts create our life experiences, and that a key to happiness is self-love. She explains that what we think, hold onto, and internalize affects our body's ability to heal itself and can create poor health.

I believe the continual process of betrayal created an act of war on my body. Ultimately this is how I uncovered what my illness came to show me.

Living inauthentically, not honoring my body's need for rest, not fulling using my voice to speak my truth. Entering relationships that did not support my well-being but rather created opportunities for me to slowly give up parts of myself. The unresolved emotion behind these choices began to rise to the surface in a way that made it impossible for me to look away. To even attempt to distract became impossible for me. The denial of who I was and suppression of a spirit meant to be free manifested themselves as myriad symptoms. It was as if my body were so tired of shouting without my listening.

If you had told me when I first became sick that the future me would have gratitude for

the inability to walk more than two feet without extreme exhaustion and pain, that I'd

somehow find the lesson in my health being stripped away, I would have said you were

crazy. When it first arrived, all my past feelings of panic, fear, and insecurity rose to the

surface like a tidal wave. I sat in the fear of it for months.

Healing doesn't mean the damage never existed. It means it can longer control our lives.

Are there parts of yourself that you have buried away or glossed over with the feeling that it's always best to keep moving forward versus dive into the feelings? If so, you are partly right. Forward movement represents action, change, evolution, and growth. However, I invite you to honor those parts of yourself that you felt were better to hide away for fear they would hinder your growth. In my experience, it became clear to me my body was asking me to bring the pain to the surface so I could heal it, make peace with it, and use it as a catalyst for growth.

THREE MANTRAS THAT CAN HELP SHIFT YOUR MINDSET AS YOU BEGIN THE HEALING PROCESS

Inhale slowly, exhale slowly, and say to yourself, "I have deep compassion and love for the parts of myself that I have chosen to hide from."

The healing process is continual and fluid, so honoring what comes up during the process of healing rather than sitting in judgement of ourselves helps to remind us we are human.

Inhale slowly, exhale slowly, and say to yourself, "I trust the healing process. I relax into a state of trust and certainty that my mind and body are healing."

Trusting ourselves and saying it aloud lets our mind and body know we mean business! By declaring our own body as a safe place where healing happens, we can easily relax into a healing state.

Inhale slowly, exhale slowly, and say to yourself, "Nothing before my own mental and physical health. It is safe to slow down and allow this time to myself for healing."

Respond to yourself the same way you would a friend or family member. Self-compassion is truly an incredible act of kindness toward ourselves.

What I know for sure about the healing process is the most beautiful version of you will be present through the whole process.

A SPACE FOR JOURNALING AND REFLECTION.

A SPACE FOR JOURNALING AND REFLECTION.

2

HEALING

CHAPTER 5

"You are worth the quiet moment. The deeper breath. You are worth the time it takes to slow down, be still, and rest."

MORGAN HARPER NICHOLS

I was flying somewhere over the Midwest on a late-night flight. It was close to midnight. The cabin was dim and quiet, mostly filled with half-asleep travelers heading home from their work obligations. It was pre-pandemic and before my chronic illness diagnosis, and I was awake and alert in what had become my normal state of too much caffeine and overworking.

At this time in my life, airplane travel for work had replaced my morning commute in my car. The concept of rest was completely foreign to me. I had been working over forty hours a week in my full-time job and running my professional organizing business on nights and weekends. I was barely giving myself time to rest and restore and was adopting a "hustle" mindset.

With the hours long, the stress intense, and the travel at times becoming disorienting to my internal clock, I would push through anyway.

"Hustle," according to Webster, is defined as "shoving, or pushing, to sell or promote energetically and aggressively, to make strenuous efforts to obtain money or business." It also mentions "to convey forcibly or hurriedly."

Take a moment and reflect on whether any of these words resonate with you in a way as something you would want to build into and become part of your life. I cringe at the idea that I felt it was necessary for me to adopt this mindset to create results. Hustle has become a buzzword that represents the idea that the more we do, the worthier we become.

Does the idea of *hard work over hustle*—in the sense that working *toward* something to promote character building, allowing space for reflection and rest, and caring for others while eliminating an aggressive approach—sound better?

Or maybe the more important question is does that *feel* better?

As I continued along with this hustle and grind attitude, I was finding myself becoming increasingly restless yet increasingly tired. In moments such as these while in flight with rest a very viable option, I always chose to ruminate on what was next: the next project, the next client, reaching outside of myself and looking for distraction. There had recently been a voice inside me longing for a place of my own. This would be the first place I would live alone, and I wanted it to be exactly as I envisioned. I was living with my parents at the time after my divorce and wanted nothing more than to rest my head in a place I could call my own.

In hindsight, my inner self knew I needed to slow down and enjoy my own personal space and privacy. A place to relax, unwind, answer to only myself, and live by my own rules. To prioritize my own self-care. The liberation in that was calling me to create a vision around this idea.

So, on that late-night flight, I began creating a list of all the features of the home I wanted for myself, compiling images around this vision.

VISION BOARDS

If you have not tried creating a vision board, it can be one of the most rewarding activities. Vision boards often consist of visual representations or images of what you want to do, be, or have in life. They can be large or small, meant to be shared or for your eyes only. The idea is you are reaching into the parts of your mind where imagination lives, simply driving your intentions and actions for the months or years ahead. They also allow you to pinpoint and create a reflection point from where you can begin to shift your focus. That shift in focus toward intentionally living, rather than lacking vision, is how we can take the next steps in creating a life we love.

"Believe it to receive it" has always been one of my mantras.

You can start creating a vision board digitally on Pinterest or cut out images from magazines and place them on a poster board. This board acts as a visual wish list and viewing it daily can start to build momentum in the direction of your dreams. It's important to also surrender to the outcomes once you have created your vision board and loosen the grip a bit on the timeline. Releasing outcomes and centering in the present moment gives us the space to dream, take action, and allow. Constantly fixating on what we want to invite into our lives can begin to carry stress with it if we are attaching our happiness to specific outcomes. Hold vision, let go, and allow.

My wish list for this space included being close to the water, with windows galore, room to entertain, and somewhere to really dig into my love of decorating. I wanted to make it fully my own. I looked at that vision board every so often before bed for three months even as I began to become ill. I never lost focus of the possibility and the voice inside me that knew this space would be positive next step for my life. I could have easily begun to list all the reasons I should stay in the comforts of my parent's home, especially as my health began to decline.

Building a relationship to self will sometimes require you to clarify what truly matters to you and what you need in your physical environment to properly heal and thrive. Then you can allow the information coming in to guide your choices. This is still a daily practice for me, but my heart has always been my greatest navigator.

A few months later on a very cold January evening at the height of my illness I left work exhausted and foggy, somehow finding any energy I could muster up to visit the home I had come across online for rent.

I walked in the door and I knew I was home. There was a dream catcher hanging by the back door and I was the last person to enter. Originated by Native Americans, specifically the Ojibwe people, dream catchers are a handmade willow hoop woven to a web or a net. They act as a spiritual tool to help assure good dreams. Personally, seeing this as a sign from the spiritual realm has always been a way for me to know I am in the right place.

The realtor was getting ready to pack up and I asked if I could take a look around. It was the only place I had looked at and I knew I was meant to be there—not for a lifetime, maybe not even beyond a year. Something inside me said this was the place I was going to heal. These were the four walls where my healing journey was going to begin. It was minutes from the water, light flooded into all the windows, and it had an attic space I could convert to a meditation and writing room. It was tiny and cozy: the perfect space for me call my own.

I signed the lease the next day and moved in one month later.

Your intuition is the most honest friend you will ever have. Lean into it.

Within weeks of moving into this home, the world slowly began to shut down. The reality of the pandemic had started to spread across the world. This home had now become my true healing bubble, and it was as if suddenly the hamster wheel I had been running on came to a screeching halt. I was fortunate enough to work from home and spent most of my time indoors curating the space in between rest.

For the first time in my adult life I had a space of my own where I could let the laundry pile up, leave dishes in the sink, and allow my bed to go unmade for days. A space where I freely let go of my perfectionism and control and allowed myself to just be. I had a hammock in the backyard I would lie in for hours, reading or listening to music. It was the calmest I had felt in years. As chronically ill as I was, this relinquishing of control felt incredibly healing for me. I knew listening to my inner knowing was the right call.

My commitment to healing my body, mind, and spirit began in that home. I had intentionally created the space to start to research nutrition and meditation techniques, diving into research on chronic illness and how chronic stress contributes to our body's immunity and capacity to repair itself. I started working with a chronic fatigue recovery group and mindset coach and fully committed myself to being open to the possibility that I could fully recover and heal. But I also begin to thrive in a way I had not allowed myself to in the past.

The most important first step I took, however, was learning how to sleep. And I began to sleep for what felt like a lifetime.

The best way to describe how it felt to commit to rest is I was finally coming home to myself.

At the onset of my chronic fatigue syndrome, I could not sleep. At all. I'd be physically and mentally exhausted throughout the day and then crawl into bed at night staring at the ceiling for hours. There were some nights I did not sleep at all. You would think with a name like "chronic fatigue" that I'd have no issue with nighttime sleep. However, I now understand my body's stress response was being activated at night. It was already highly activated throughout the day because of high levels of stress, and I was doing nothing to regulate my nervous system—other than react to it with more stress. This cycle caused continuous sleepless nights and myriad additional health issues.

In short, when you are deprived of sleep, your sympathetic nervous system activity increases, which is also mirrored by an increase in blood pressure. So, the result is simply a lack of sleep. All this prompted me to fully understand how to better my sleep cycle and learn more about why we sleep. Turns out there are so many really good things that go on in these intelligent bodies of ours when we switch off for the night. The book *Why We Sleep*, by Matthew Walker, PhD, was *the game changer* for me.

Have you ever thought about why your body needs an adequate night's sleep? Virtually every part of the body changes during sleep. It begins to reinforce the cardiovascular and immune systems and helps to regulate metabolism. Consider it your body's repair mode time. As I began to understand how my lack of proper rest and high stress levels were contributing to my illness over time, I then was able to honor my need for a restful night's sleep.

I can now sleep soundly for anywhere from eight to ten hours per night. For the first time in my adult life, my body has found its natural sleep rhythm also called the circadian rhythm.

My nightly routine has become a nonnegotiable in my life. The moment I felt my body wanting to rest, I would simply listen and take a nap, close my eyes, or head to bed even, if it was only 7:00 p.m. Gradually my body would naturally fall asleep and wake up without an alarm. I truly felt rested for the first time.

You might be saying to yourself that finding a sleep routine is not as easy for you. I am not naive to the fact that daily stressors exist and look quite different for all of us. Aside from balancing our family responsibilities, and work, we have been moving through a time when we are living with a heightened fear response as the news can become increasingly alarming and negative to take in.

So I call you to reflect on asking yourself how much you can gain if you consider starting to dedicate time to better rest.

Why not start now?

Finding your own unique way to commit to rest can be one of the greatest acts of self-love.

CONSIDER WHAT LACK OF SLEEP DOES TO THE BODY

According to Dr. Teofilo Lee-Chiong, chief medical liaison at Philips Sleep and Respiratory Care, "Sleep and the immune system are bidirectionally linked and both have important roles in the body's defense against diseases. Optimal immune function requires adequate sleep, and inadequate sleep impairs the immune response."

Sleep deprivation lowers performance: lower productivity, social fluidity, rational decision-making, memory recall, emotional control, immune system function, and even a response to flu vaccine.

A sleep-deprived person can be considered legally drunk when driving because of the impairment on the brain.

Quality of life can be affected as it becomes less likely you would want to participate in normal activities.

WHAT HELPED MY SLEEP, AND SOME OF MY NIGHTLY ROUTINE TIPS

With the recommendation from my doctor I began taking small amounts of magnesium supplements. Magnesium increases GABA, which encourages relaxation as well as sleep. Magnesium also plays a role in regulating the body's stress response system.

I do my best to switch off all electronics one hour before bed, as the light can restrain the production of melatonin, the hormone that controls our sleep.

I will read or do some journaling thirty minutes before I am ready to sleep. This helps to relax my brain without the overstimulation of the television or scrolling on my phone. I also never read news articles or watch the news at night.

Sleep meditation, breath work, and listening to sleep stories helped me for many months get into a relaxed state while settling in for the night. Some of my favorites are through the Calm app.

Finding ways to regulate my nervous system throughout the day, such as meditation and being mindful of my thoughts, has allowed my body to fall into a restful sleep. With my fight-or-flight response dial turned all the way down I can access my natural state of calm and ease.

I always pour myself a cup of Bedtime Yogi Tea, which has the perfect blend of herbal tea that creates a natural relaxed state within the body. The secret ingredient is valerian root, which is dubbed nature's valium.

Lavender is one of my favorite scents as it promotes relaxation—yes, it's been proven. I always spray a bit on my pillow before bed and add a few drops to my oil diffuser about an hour before I sleep. Be sure to research which essential oils are nontoxic. An article titled "How to Choose Non-toxic Essential Oil Diffusers" in Heal Hard helped me find the perfect one. I also find taking a warm bath with all-natural lavender bath salts mixed with magnesium really promotes great sleep. Always be mindful of whether the oils or sprays you are using are toxic if you have any pets.

It's always best to consult with your doctor if you are experiencing frequent insomnia or the inability to have a restful night and it is interfering with your daily life. However, these are some of my tips that have helped me naturally find my way to a good night's sleep.

Give yourself permission to unplug and regroup without feeling guilty. Sometimes the most productive thing you can do for yourself and others is relax and restore. It is hard to be our best running on empty. Rest is not the absence of activity but the presence of peace and well-being, and it can truly be the starting point of your healing journey.

A SPACE FOR JOURNALING AND REFLECTION.

A SPACE FOR JOURNALING AND REFLECTION.

CHAPTER 6

"And I said to my body. I want to be your friend. It took a long breath and replied, I have been waiting my whole life for this."

NAYYIRAH WAHEED

Have you ever thought about the day you were born? The moment you arrived in the world?

You may have learned the details of your birth based on the memories of your parents, family members, or caregivers. The story they captured in their mind's eye on the day of your birth. Their perception and a recounting of a time in their lives, mirrored back to you through a story told with myriad emotions. Or it could be you don't have the details of that moment. You simply knew you arrived and have existed in your body ever since. Moving through this world with the details is a mystery, an untold story left for wonder and curiosity.

It is hard not to argue childhood experiences influence our lives in so many ways: who we become, our perceptions, reality, and even our health. But what about how we got here? There is evidence the body remembers.

You might be thinking that is a wild claim, but take a moment to consider what Annie Brook, PhD, a somatic therapist whose work dives into psychology and body-based therapy, has to say regarding her years of research. She has found the body remembers our birth experience and there are parts of the brain that literally create a file cabinet of experiences. In her studies she has found someone's birth story, whether peaceful or traumatic, could carry weight throughout their life and play out through their subconscious mind. However, we have the power to retell the story if it is in fact traumatic or damaging to hear.

In February of 1978, just a few short weeks after one of the worst blizzards in the history of the Northeast, I showed up in the world. The day I arrived was not met with the most peaceful imagery. I was swept away in the arms of the nurses the moment I exited my mother's womb. My delicate lungs were not ready for the world around me. Unable to breathe on my own, I was placed in an incubator for weeks before I was not able to breathe without the assistance of oxygen. It was also taxing on my organs, particularly my heart, as my infant body was gaining the strength to develop a healthy set of lungs.

My parents, leaning on their traditional and deep faith in Catholicism, asked that a priest perform a baptism as the doctors were repeatedly telling them I wasn't going to make it through the night. Prayers were recited; faith and fear circled the room. Uncertainty was present.

Annie Brook's work would suggest a birthing infant's brain can record pressure and stress. Precognitive events have no context to an infant, so the brain does exactly what it is wired to do, which is shift into a state of anxiety related to a perceived danger based on the environment. The question is always, "How could something I have no memory of influence my life now?" It seems our brains record these moments and they can become a part of our experience as we begin to grow.

Here is the story I prefer to tell. Before I could see, before I could cry out, before I could be held in my parent's arms, I was being asked by the universe to breathe. Some may prefer to call it a higher power, or human instinct, or simply the science of the human body. In my mind I was being asked to rely on my body's intelligence to slowly gain strength and heal. Upon my arrival into this world I was being asked to fight to stay in it. And I did.

Yet somehow the story of "I was strong enough to keep going" changed. Growing up I never felt safe, connected to trusting of my body. I had frequent stomachaches as a child and fixated on my health in a way to suggest that something was always wrong. I would get dropped off at slumber parties and want to go home in fear I would suddenly become sick. I clung to the safety of my home and felt it was a way to retreat from the outside world, as home was a safe space.

Reading through my journals I kept as a child from the age of eight until about ten years old, there was a common theme in which I would talk about how I got strep throat, or a stomach bug, or generally didn't feel good.

Whenever an event was coming up like a holiday, family vacation, or dance recital, I would obsess over getting sick and not being able to enjoy my time or attend. This obsession led to anxious thoughts and a heightened stress response. This carried out fully into my adult life. Before any new job or life event, I would become sick and tell myself the same story over and over. I vividly remember my grandparents taking me to the doctor on a family trip to Disney with another throat infection and even missing my senior class photo because of a bug. I cringe at the thought of these memories.

Jen Mann, mind-body practitioner and cofounder of the CFS School, explains that chronic illness develops because of the nervous system being stuck, over a long period of time, in survival mode. Survival mode is activated by a continuous high level of perceived threat, alert, and alarm in the mind and body. And in survival mode your immune, endocrine, lymphatic, digestive, and cardiovascular systems are not functioning at their best. Over time, being stuck in chronic survival mode can cause chronic sickness and susceptibility to viruses.

In essence, nothing is inherently wrong. Your nervous system is simply stuck thinking it needs to keep protecting you.

"I don't have a strong immune system."

"My body doesn't work as well as other people's."

"I will get sick if I don't rest enough."

These were the stories I told myself for decades of my life.

As you can imagine, when my body developed chronic illness, I initially felt fully validated in my thinking. It was as if the story I had been telling myself throughout my entire life was true. That I was not worthy of being healthy, vibrant, or capable of living a full life. I fully believed I was not safe in my body, and that my body was always working against me and attacking itself.

I had fully manifested poor health in part because of a lifetime of thinking I was not worthy of good health. It truly took this rock bottom health crisis and my inability to function because of poor health to finally undo years of playing the victim around my health. I had to start with trusting my body and understanding what it needed.

The truth is you have a choice.

What impacted you does not have to define you or determine your future. You can choose healing and growth and access this at any time in your journey. Your body is strong and capable. You are not broken. Sometimes we are just in progress, in process, and moving through a transition.

This is how I began to see my health: a slow and steady process on the road to healing.

DISMANTLING THE NEGATIVE THOUGHTS

One of the first steps I took toward regaining my health and dismantling years of negative thinking about my body was to understand and uncover my relationship with food. Intuitive eating is truly about finding a way to eat that is sustainable and healthy rather than researching the perfect diet plan or experimenting with new food rules that exist in the world of diet culture.

Diet culture has become a toxic concept that implies there is something wrong with our bodies in the sense of the way we look. It assumes certain foods are bad and we are bad for eating them. It has an element of shame around it that can cause us to move away from the most important element of food, which is to promote our *health.*

As an adult I would eat in a rush and be super caffeinated to take care of feeling tired. The easier the recipe the faster it would land on the plate, and I thought this was a win for me. I was not honoring my need for rest or the importance of *nourishment.* I had never made the connection that the food we eat literally fuels our body and is meant for good health and immunity and supports almost every function in our body to work properly. A healthy outside truly starts with the insides.

Here are some questions to ask yourself if you are exploring your own relationship with food and how it might be impacting your overall health.

How will I feel in my body after this meal?

I had come to realize that certain foods were perpetuating my fatigue and slowing me down, so I began to pay attention to how I was feeling in my body after a particular meal. I even began to journal about it in a way that supported my well-being and felt it was truly an act of love toward my body to pay attention to the messages it was sending.

What food choices can I make that are satisfying and filling?

Eating only one type of food consistently because it's your favorite doesn't allow for a variety of foods that can help support your wellness. For example, I loved pasta, so I would eat it at least four nights a week, not giving my body the opportunity to take in some vegetables, fruits, or proteins. I began to balance out my nutritional intake in a more conscious way.

Am I genuinely enjoying this meal while I eat?

One of the first things I was asked to do by a naturopathic doctor was to slow down while I was eating, chew slowly, and never eat in front of the television. Looking back, I was eating in a hurry for years and never truly enjoying my meals. I started sitting at my kitchen table with my phone off, simply enjoying my meals. It became a moment that I could tune in and show appreciation for my food and how it was truly supporting my body.

How much water did I drink today?

Staying hydrated will not only positively affect your mental function, but it will help with tiredness, headaches, and mood changes. Since 70 percent of your body is made up of water, it is so essential we maintain these levels that help our vital organs. Inherently, I knew the importance of hydration but would go all day barely drinking! I started drinking close to three liters of water per day and began to feel my body was truly waking up to the hydration.

I also began getting real about my gut health and how it was impacting my health. Our gut stores over one hundred trillion good and bad bacteria, and the incorrect mix of microbiota can lead to all kinds of health issues. Those microbes within our intestinal tract interact with our mind and can worsen fatigue, anxiety, and even pain.

In my attempt to begin reversing decades of gut health issues, I came across Anthony William, otherwise known as the Medical Medium. I was watching a YouTube video in which he was raving about how ingesting raw celery juice every morning will lead to all kinds of miraculous healing. Having just been diagnosed with chronic fatigue syndrome, I would have tried anything, even if he had said to tie celery stalks to my head and run around in circles.

So I was jumping on the celery juice train.

I purchased an inexpensive juicer by Aicok. It's basic for my needs, however there are a host of others that deliver more juicing benefits depending upon how often you plan on juicing. I picked up roughly eight packages of organic celery and found that one and a half stalks make about sixteen ounces, which was my starting point. Then the morning juicing began. Note this is best done on an empty stomach first thing in the morning, after a glass of water.

Here's what I noticed after about one week.

- My skin was noticeably clearer, and I had a smoother complexion.

- My energy dipped less in the afternoon. Living with CFS/ME was like an energy roller coaster with extreme dips. I felt a bit steadier throughout the day.

Since then, I have started drinking up to thirty-two ounces in the morning, and yes it has helped to heal my digestion, which for me has been quite amazing.

The celery juice was just the beginning of my health journey in terms of where I started with changing my food choices. I have overhauled my diet by eliminating processed foods, gluten, and dairy along the way. I can attest that my energy has sustained throughout the day, and my digestion has improved. It ignited a confidence in me: for the first time I felt safe and balanced in my body, knowing my body supports me and wants me to feel good.

So, what's in this magic green potion? Here's the simplest explanation.

As William explains in his book *Celery Juice*, there are sodium cluster salts. These sodium cluster salts starve and fight off unwanted pathogens and bacteria—troublemakers responsible for a tremendous number of symptoms and conditions, including autoimmune diseases—and neutralize toxins, which are another key contributor to all kinds of illnesses. They also restore hydrochloric acid over time and help the liver to produce bile, both of which are critical not only for strong digestion but to help kill off pathogens.

Celery juice has now become part of my morning routine, and I know my body is thanking me for it.

My nutritional choices have become a way of life for me and a commitment to my health and overall well-being. If you are rediscovering how to better support your body and provide it with what it needs to thrive, please remember this journey is yours and yours only. When I first began along this path to wellness through food, I found myself apologizing to family and friends for having to bring my own food with me to family gatherings or to the waitress when I needed to ask questions about how the food was prepared. But as I began to regain my health, my inner critic stopped speaking, and I felt empowered by my choices.

You do not need to apologize for honoring your health and wanting to improve your life in any way. You are worthy of a healthy body and can learn to trust yourself and the way you feel in your body.

MANTRAS FOR A WELLNESS MINDSET

Here are some mantras they can help you along in your own unique path to wellness, specifically meant to help gain confidence around rebuilding your health. I placed these throughout my home on Post-it Notes as I was beginning to dismantle years of negative thoughts regarding my body's ability to heal and thrive.

Every single one of my cells is filled with wellness, health, and vitality.

All my cells know what to do in order to heal.

I release all unease from my body and welcome health, love, and happiness into my life.

My body is strong and capable.

I feel healthier every day.

I am grateful for my health.

Repeating these daily upon waking up and getting into bed can help begin to shift your mindset. These simple mantras help to shift your focus away from the old story and refocus the brain toward a positive experience. These are certainly not a magic wand for instant healing, but they helped me adapt into a new way of thinking *as I took conscious action* toward loving and accepting my body as a healthy place.

You are wired for healing and are worthy of a positive life experience in your body. It is very empowering when we discover that a past story we told ourselves is no longer serving us and decide to move toward writing a new one. The brain can recover and wants to be in perfect balance and ease.

Recognition that every single thought, feeling, and emotion, whether tied to a painful past event or trauma that stayed with you, is simply a transient emotion will shift your energy. The anxiety I lived with around my health was very real and I believe associated with my birthing story, but allowing myself to have discernment and awareness that my body was a healing force gave me the tools to heal.

Do you believe healing happens? Me too.

A SPACE FOR JOURNALING AND REFLECTION.

A SPACE FOR JOURNALING AND REFLECTION.

CHAPTER 7

"You are not required to set yourself on fire to keep other people warm."

UNKNOWN

In the summer of '93 I kissed someone else's boyfriend at the movies. I was fifteen, had my first major crush, and wanted attention.

These choices are always the best indicators of unhealed wounds and the problem is not always rooted in the action you took but in the motivation behind them.

Have you ever wanted to go back and change one reaction and choice you made when you were younger that seems so insignificant as an adult but at the time that choice set off a trajectory of life experience that shifted a period in your life? One that years later offered itself as an opportunity for reflection and compassion for self? One that allowed you to understand parts of yourself that needed to come to the surface to be healed so it could be clear what is most important to you?

What followed this innocent kissing event was the first time I would experience being bullied, shamed, and belittled by my peers. I entered high school that fall and was told by a group of girls who cornered me in the bathroom that even if they were ever nice to me I should remember they all secretly hated me would make sure nobody else liked me for what I did.

I know this sounds like a scene out of *Mean Girls*, and for decades it has been a laughable moment, but at the time I was devastated. I did not want to go to school, I obsessed over how I looked, and I was fearful that anyone who acted like a friend didn't like me for me. School became a source of stress for me so I did anything to fit in. Throwing parties when my parents were away, being agreeable on every topic even if I felt differently. Popularity and attention became the only social element I fixated on. This behavior set the tone for my high school days as some of the most anxiety-driven years of my teenage life.

I held onto shame, embarrassment, and regret over kissing that boy for dear life. It's heartbreaking to go back in time in my mind and revisit the younger version of me during those years. Sometimes I wonder if it's even helpful or therapeutic to relive experiences that created a hurtful imprint on our young hearts. But I have learned that the best we can do is hold deep compassion for the version of ourselves that existed before we were confident and brave enough to make more aligned choices.

Evolutionary psychologist Frank T. McAndrew in his article for *The Guardian*, "Why are High School memories burned into our brains?," suggests, "The main driver is the collision between the hardwiring of our brains that took place across several millions of years of evolution and the odd social bubble created by high school, which poses an unprecedented social challenge to our prehistoric minds." So, blame our caveman brains? To take this a step further there is something memory researchers describe as the *reminiscence bump*. It's the tendency for older adults (over forty) to have increased or enhanced recollection for events that occurred during their adolescence and early adulthood. That seems to explain why that song that was playing every time you and your pals were out driving around at sixteen immediately brings back vivid memories of those moments.

Not realizing the lasting hurt "the incident" would have on my high school years, in retrospect I lacked the tools to understand that nobody had the right to judge our actions from a place of cruelty or shame. We don't have to believe what anyone says as truth. Sure, I did something foolish but that did not mean I had to buy into the bullying.

Someone's opinion of you is not your reality unless you believe it.

Their words are powerless without your acknowledgment. This holds true from the innocent actions we take in our youth to our adult life. It doesn't negate personal responsibility but rather acts as a reflection point to uncover our self-worth and sense of belonging.

What I never did was speak up for myself or dive deeper into my actions of the *motivation* behind these people-pleasing actions such as why I craved the attention in the first place. I also did not want to appear argumentative and deemed it as a threat if I were to stand in my power and stand up for myself.

In my youth, I compressed, shut down, edited my words, and overcompensated by trying to be liked. A subconscious terror grew with the fear I would seem harsh and abrasive and possibly disliked if I stood in my power. And on I went never wanting to rock the boat. In friendships, relationships, and jobs, it played out well into my adult life. I gave away my precious power to everyone for fear of being disliked.

I fell into the trap that women should not speak too loudly or take up space when they have something important to share, because that might have meant I wasn't worthy of being liked.

These people-pleasing behaviors were rooted in fear—notably, the fear of rejection.

When I became chronically ill, it was clear I was so scared of offending people that this fear became trapped emotions. I used pain and symptoms to speak for myself so I did not have to use my voice. I held these emotional triggers in my body.

The most common way people give up their power is by thinking they don't have any. When we consistently suppress our emotions and hold back our words for validation and approval from others, we continuously give our power away.

You have a lot more power than you are giving yourself credit for. Please embrace it.

In fact, you are powerful beyond your wildest dreams, and you are entitled to call that power back in each time you catch yourself giving it away. Your power lies in your ability to witness when you are people pleasing and then set boundaries which are born of your values.

And your values are those precious gems that make up who you are. How you find and tap into your values can at times be tricky, as it was for me. Other times they are inherently known and easy for us to access.

The clearer your values are to you, the easier it becomes to make decisions from a place of knowing and being able to clearly create healthy boundaries around how you are being treated, what you tolerate from others, and simply what your likes and dislikes are without feeling the need to apologize or explain.

I found my voice and began to set boundaries with others when I became chronically ill. Suddenly I had to advocate for my health throughout my recovery, questioning my doctors when I felt dismissed or misunderstood and consistently letting family and friends know what I needed to get better. I even would ask my employer if I could work from home as I rebuilt my strength. Each time I stood up for myself and spoke my truth about what I needed for my health, I slowly began to build a strong foundation for myself by using my voice and understanding my values.

I knew that with my health suddenly becoming my number-one priority, shifting my life around in new ways was going to seem odd to others, who had become accustomed to my lack of boundaries specifically around that time. I was always answering work emails after hours, pushing myself to stay out late despite being tired, and scheduling around my clients' needs versus my own.

The first thing I learned to do was a practice in not giving away my power. This was a tough one for me, as I had been living this way for so long.

Here are some of the ways I learned to slowly shift away from people pleasing which created a clear landscape for me to understand and lean into boundary setting and my values. You can begin to incorporate these into your life if you find yourself struggling to say no.

Allow other people to be responsible for their emotions.

We don't have to take responsibility for other people's emotions. I repeat this to myself daily. It is of course important to be aware of how you speak to others and know that your actions do affect others, but it is not up to you to manage how they feel. This kind of took the pressure off me a bit in the sense that I realized people's perceptions are nothing more than their own inner reality shaped by their life experience. Guess what? That has nothing to do with you!

Acknowledge your choices.

I would complain quite a bit whenever I said yes and meant no, spiraling into self-pity. Then I would realize I could decide and have a say in the matters of my own life. Everything is a choice, from the job you take, to the people you surround yourself with, to the power that you give to the words that others speak to you. Acknowledging your place and say in all of it empowers you to make choices that are in line with who you are.

Say no without explaining.

Try this on for size for one month and see how it feels. If you are asked to head out with a friend for dinner and your body is gently asking that you stay in, it is okay to say no without getting into every detail about why you want to stay in. When you catch yourself overexplaining, simply stop, take a breath, and remember that you are safe to respond with a simple answer. You are not responsible for the reactions from others. I still struggle with this one myself, but it has gotten easier and has become very freeing in the process.

These three pillars were the starting point for me to begin to set boundaries and realize the only people who get upset about you setting boundaries are the ones who were benefiting from your not having any.

To my surprise, most people in my life understood and were happy to give me what I needed to create space for my health. The boundary setting practice gifted me the ability to use discernment in establishing new relationships and reevaluating my life choices. I also now understand that we won't always vibe with everyone, and that is okay. My social circle is tiny, yet it's built on a solid foundation of quality and safety.

And I finally understand my two core values.

CORE VALUES EXPLAINED

In Brené Brown's book *Dare to Lead*, she presents a list of values. The list includes over one hundred values such as excellence, family, joy, giving back, and patience. She explains that reducing our list to just two core values is universally difficult, as most identify with close to ten or twenty. However, with too many to focus on, nothing becomes the true driver of our actions.

I decided to commit to understanding and uncovering my two core values and use these as the basis for my life choices and decisions so I could move forward without explanation or second-guessing myself. More importantly, I could feel grounded and confident in my decisions and once and for all stop the people pleasing. The book *Dare to Lead* truly acted as a guide for me to understand what was driving my choices and gain clarity on my future self and find my way out of the dark. It helped define who I am at my core.

The three questions to ask yourself when uncovering your core values according to Brown in her book:

1. Does this define me?
2. Is this who I am at my best?
3. Is this a filter that I use to make hard decisions?

These exercises in Brown's book changed my life. I took me a few days to narrow it down, and I had to sleep on it a few nights. I suppose a part of me that I never witnessed or gave love to was being asked to reveal itself, as I was always putting others before myself.

My two core values are authenticity and independence. Whenever I practiced these throughout my life, I felt the most understood, free, and at peace. My nervous system is calm, I am more focused, and my mood is stabilized.

Examples of this are found in the small professional organizing business I had started. This work allowed me to tap into my love of helping others in their homes by creating spaces that are representative of their lives yet streamlined and clutter free to allow for mindfulness and peace. It was a dream of mine to be able to create the freedom to work for myself while also practicing work that I felt passionate about. Freedom and authenticity are clearly the driving force behind that choice.

Another example is how my life has opened up with more time for me to spend in nature, one of my favorite places to be. Since I have begun to be intentional about what I say yes to, I opened time in my week to connect with the outdoors. I dedicate time on the weekends and a few hours during the week to sit and watch the sunset, go hiking, explore nature, and log off all electronics.

It was clearer to me why my body had acted out with so many symptoms when these core values were revealed. For most of my life, I was not making choices that honored or reflected this, as I have revealed in past chapters.

From this knowing, I now have hard conversations when my values are in question. Having hard conversations with others when my values are not being met still makes my face flush, particularly asking for what I need around honoring my rest. My heart sometimes begins to beat faster, and I slowly and lovingly have to let myself know that I am safe over and over to honor and be myself. Essentially, I am rewiring my brain to respond.

WHY DO VALUES MATTER?

They are the principles and standards that shape your decisions and behaviors. It is not hard to make decisions when you know what your values are and stand in the truth of who you are.

> *"A value is a way of being or believing that we hold most important. Living into our values means that we do more than profess our values, we practice them. We walk our talk- we are clear about what we believe and hold important, and we take care that our intentions, words, thoughts, and behaviors align with those beliefs."*
>
> BRENÉ BROWN

DAILY MANTRAS FOR LIVING IN YOUR VALUES (REPEAT AS NEEDED)

I know who I am, I understand my values, and I practice them with ease and confidence.

I live each day by honoring my values, and it is safe to honor my needs.

I am consciously creating a beautiful life by standing in my power and communicating my needs.

I am worthy of asking for what I need.

By practicing my values, I am honoring my mental and physical health.

A SPACE FOR JOURNALING AND REFLECTION.

A SPACE FOR JOURNALING AND REFLECTION.

CHAPTER 8

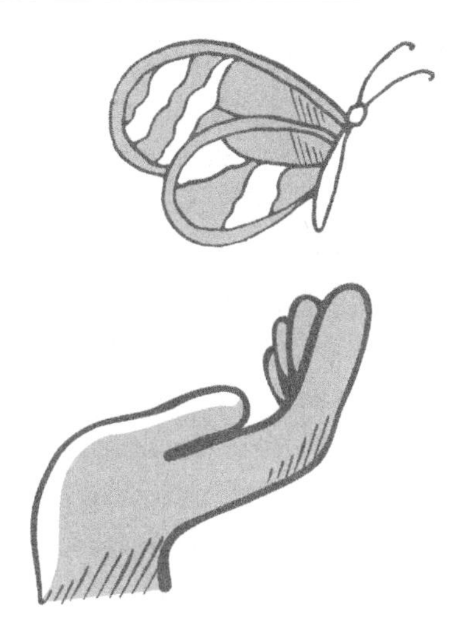

"You have to say I am forgiven again and again, until it becomes the story you believe about yourself."

CHERYL STRAYED

"Can't I work on forgiving others who have hurt me and just move on from all this *self- forgiveness* talk?"

It was a Saturday morning and I was curled up on my couch with a hot cup of tea. I was on my routine virtual 10:00 a.m. meeting with my therapist. It was only a few months into the pandemic in the summer of 2020 and a few short months into my deep healing journey, as I began recovering my body from chronic illness. Self-forgiveness was a topic I had been avoiding.

I would go days without leaving the house. I was working from home and it seemed I was beginning to pick and choose the inner work I wanted to do on myself. My body was responding well to the healthy food choices, the sleep routine, and the lounging in my hammock for hours. I loved the new freedom I had created in my life in terms of living alone and having the time and space to heal. For the first time in many years I felt a sense of freedom and happiness I had never known. My body and mind welcomed my new schedule and the sense of ease that came with a quiet and calm life.

Yet when the deep inner work had come up around self-forgiveness, my body would flare into pain symptoms and exhaustion, causing me to feel a sense of defeat and sadness. I now understand it was a nervous system response to memories and emotions living in my mind, and they needed to be faced.

As our mind replays a certain scene that happened in our life that triggers an emotional response, our brain will begin to fire away signals to the body that we are not safe. It is nearly impossible however to heal our body from this response if the nervous system, brain, and body do not feel safe. Understanding this connection shifted my approach to self-forgiveness so I could finally begin to heal. Essentially, I had to change the narrative in my mind around painful emotions and feelings of being unsafe to self-compassion, love, and forgiveness.

When was the last time you forgave yourself? Not forgiveness for the person who may have wronged you, or hurt you, but forgave yourself?

I believe self-forgiveness may be one of the most difficult tasks assigned to the human condition. It is not for the faint of heart. Forgiveness could be for the small mistake you made at work that has been keeping you up at night. For falling back into the relationship that you know isn't healthy for you. Maybe even breaking small promises to yourself daily around your self-care and well-being.

Or maybe for the pain you held onto for so long from a past situation that you buried away.

How often do you sabotage yourself over choices you've made or obsess over wanting situations to have gone differently? This was a narrative that kept me in the same loop for so many years: wondering how my life could have been different if I had just made a different choice and not took that job or had made those irresponsible financial choices or stayed in that toxic relationship for so long.

I have found sometimes it is easier to forgive others than it is to forgive ourselves and let go of our own mistakes.

As I continued my path to wellness and began to slowly understand the importance of self-care as it relates to self-love and a deep sense of worthiness, I knew I had to forgive myself for the pain I had caused myself. For ignoring my intuition for so many years, for choosing others before my own mental wellness, and for not properly taking care of my body. At this point in my life, I had seen firsthand the consequences of my actions when choosing so many things above my own happiness, as they negatively affected my health for decades. This was the motivation to stop the cycle and move into self-forgiveness.

This would require reaching into my past self and reliving uncomfortable moments that I did not want to face. My personal path to self-forgiveness was met with many failed attempts until I finally understood the importance and change that would occur within my mental and physical health once I was able to self-forgive.

The turning point was hearing something my therapist said.

"The only way out is through. You did the best you could in those times of your life with the level of awareness that you had. You are on a different playing field now, Lauren. It's time to forgive yourself, heal, and move forward."

Hearing "you are on a different playing field" allowed me to take a step back and see my life from a new perspective. I was now consciously making choices from a place of knowing and understanding what was best for me. I was nurturing my body with good food, getting plenty of rest, and educating and empowering myself on how to naturally heal my body. I was moving toward a more fully aligned life in service of me.

It seemed only logical that the next step was to go through this lesson in self-forgiveness.

You are meant to do this inner work and walk yourself right into it, not fly over it or dig your way underneath it. Right through it. Through the fire, the pain, the fear.

To forgive is to set a prisoner free and discover the prisoner was you.

In the beginning of doing the inner work to self-forgive and reach deep into the parts of ourselves, where so much shame, embarrassment, self-criticism, self-resentment, and discomfort live, it can feel like a dysfunctional relationship about to end without closure. You know in your heart closure doesn't always need lengthy conversation, explanation, or answers to questions left unsaid, but the absence of these things sits in your body with the weight of a thousand bricks.

The tidal wave of emotion I carried in my body from not releasing past pain and hurt was like witnessing a tsunami of fear, heaviness, loss, and confusion. When the wanting to release it became greater than the pain of carrying it, I knew I had to let it go.

I don't believe we are ever seeking the dismal energy that pain carries with it or want to welcome its disruptive entrance. But you will come to a point when you want to personally see it to the door.

Keep walking toward that door.

Before you are ready for the pain to exit, remember you are about to quiet the dark storm it carries, and you are consciously replacing it with shiny glimmers of hope.

Sit in silence and breathe into that hope. Have compassion for yourself and know you did your best. That is when you know the pain has been lifted: when you can see the past mistakes and give love to the parts of yourself that may have made mistakes.

The hope is simply to remind you that a million shining stars are visible in the darkest night.

In those moment of self-forgiveness where I was so grateful that I had found the strength to release the pain, there was a small part of me that knew after this had settled, I would be grateful for those moments that I had made mistakes. Instead of a fist, I offered the past hurt a goodbye embrace. Standing in gratitude that I was still able to see the goodness, the light, and hold an incredible willingness to keep going despite uncertainty.

The mistakes were heavy, but the forgiveness brought an incredible moment of honesty and clarity.

Always remember new worlds are born and built from the damage that is done. There are treasures yet to be uncovered.

Every goodbye carries with it a lesson. And sometimes, the best light is that seen from a burning bridge.

Yes, I am talking about saying goodbye to the pain that was carried in your heart from any mistakes or regrets you may have, just as you would say goodbye to a person or a job when you are moving onto something that is more nourishing and uplifting for your soul.

The relationship we have with ourselves is the most difficult relationship to nurture. We're programmed to put others first. We should be taught from the very beginning about valuing our own worth. People who practice self-love rarely start wars within themselves. They think about their well-being and honor their choices through a deep understanding of self.

It has always been fascinating to me how we know so well how to give love to the hurting parts within us yet never to the parts of ourselves that need the most love.

Yet once you know how to be in a relationship with yourself, all the rest will be easy. Your stock is so high you'd never sell it to anyone for a bargain price, or in turn, value anyone else unfairly.

The problem is we are sometimes in an adversarial relationship with ourselves, and that makes it difficult to see that we are worthy of self-forgiveness.

The beginning of any journey toward self-forgiveness is to decide that yes, you are worth releasing from the prison of guilt, shame, and pain, and you are going to actively participate in your own freedom.

It's like wanting anything else—once you decide you can't live without it, *how* you're going to get it becomes a detail.

And guess what? *You're not really living when you can't forgive yourself.* It's a trap so insidious that sometimes we barely know we're in it. Everything seems fine until you read the fine print on your soul.

Choosing to forgive yourself doesn't mean you are weak, in fact it represents a new level of strength that says you are willing to accept the actions and behaviors that need forgiveness, versus continuing to ignore them or self-sabotage. It is understanding you are willing to move on, regardless of the past and finally letting go of all the emotions tied to a specific event or time period.

This is making amends with yourself and restoring trust. It is also opening up a new path to move forward, as you no longer ruminate on past choices.

Acknowledge your true feelings, thoughts, and beliefs about yourself and surrender them so you can begin to bring in the self-compassion needed for this practice.

WHY IT MATTERS TO YOUR MENTAL HEALTH

Your mental health is essential to your well-being. It plays a vital role in your decision-making and even your problem-solving skills. Forgiveness is truly a choice that says you want what is best for yourself and a reminder that you have to sometimes make tough choices and go through consequences to see the results.

HOW TO ACTIVELY BEGIN SELF-FORGIVENESS

Begin by taking out a piece of paper and writing down your decision to forgive yourself for whatever is weighing you down.

Notice the feelings of resistance. *Breathe.* You'll still be *you*, only a more alive *you*, once you let go of this burden.

"I, (insert name here), choose to actively participate in my own freedom. I choose to forgive myself for (insert all sins here)."

That was the hardest part of the exercise. Who will you be without your pain? The person with no pain. It's that simple and is a large part of why we don't let go. This pain is familiar, and you understand yourself within this context. By holding this in your body for so long, it begins to become uncomfortable as it rises to the surface to be let go.

You have just observed your ego struggling with its own identity. Release the burden of self-directed blame and shame.

When I went through this practice, I needed to do it again and again to truly sit and release the guilt I had built up in my body and tap into shifting this energy from sadness to uplifting and forward movement. Forgiveness can't be forced. It can't be artificial. Simply continue the practice again and again and let the words work gradually in their own way.

I even created a ritual around my self-forgiveness practice. I would sit in a comfortable spot in my home, light some candles, and put on some music to calm my nervous system. I saw this as letting my insides know I was fully committed to letting go. I would then write out the things I was forgiving myself for in my journal and do this practice just before bed.

When I finally felt I had released all the shame, guilt, and pain, I took the pages from my journal, ripped them out, and drove to the beach, where I burned them by the ocean. The act of burning was representative of finally releasing from my heart to the paper to then being fully released.

SELF-FORGIVENESS AFFIRMATIONS

I am worthy of forgiveness.

Self-compassion encourages me to learn and grow.

I can simultaneously give myself
grace and accountability.

I believe I did the best I could with what I knew,
who I was, and the resources I had at the time.

I accept myself completely.

Today, I start fresh.

In time you can make this forgiveness ritual and the affirmations a regular part of your life, letting go of anything weighing on your heart and opening your heart to each new moment with a wise and loving kindness. I see the practice of self-forgiveness as a lifelong ritual, one that is essential to our emotional well-being. It truly allows us to release burdensome emotions again and again and gives our body the ability to self-regulate our emotions and create safety and calm.

The word itself says for*giving*. And you are deserving of giving yourself as much love and compassion that you could ever imagine for yourself.

A SPACE FOR JOURNALING AND REFLECTION.

A SPACE FOR JOURNALING AND REFLECTION.

3

AWAKENING

CHAPTER 9

"Let it all go, see what stays."

KASSANDRA VAUGHN

I have a tattoo on my left wrist that says "Let it Be" with a small peace sign. It's been there long enough to be a bit faded and blurry but the message is permanently inked onto my wrist because I need to see it every day. I got it in my midthirties when I was searching for meaning and peace in my life. I suppose I am always searching for those things somehow but I needed a reminder on my body that I could look at daily. I still stop and breathe when I see it.

The reminder is an act of allowing things to play out as they are meant to, to be an active participant in our lives but remembering that clinging to outcomes, future goals, and what-if scenarios never allow us to truly move forward. Even as I type this, it reminds me that this must become a daily practice.

Ask yourself, what would happen if I just let go?

Letting go is not something you do.

It is something you stop doing.

No matter the fixation—

be it possessions, people, or prosperity, attachment always leads to suffering.

JOSHUA FIELDS MILLBURN

I want to take the pressure off you for a moment when contemplating this question. There is no pot of gold at the end of the rainbow. There is no reason to be reaching for anything outside of yourself that will suddenly make your life whole, complete, and amazing. If you are like most people, the idea of letting go could be hard to consider, as we are all holding onto something in our lives, be it tangible or intangible.

Have you ever found yourself holding on so tightly to an outcome that you never asked yourself to consider what would happen if it didn't play out exactly as you planned? This was one of the hardest things for me to grasp as I began to heal my body from chronic illness. I had to suddenly accept what was and let the outcome just be. It was one of scariest yet most interesting places to be in my life. This is in no way giving up or throwing in the towel. In fact, it is the opposite. It is being open to new possibilities.

When I was in the season of my life when the illness was debilitating, I would say things like, "When I'm well, my life is going to be so much better."

While I can certainly step into my life with more energy, vibrancy, and brain power, this journey has not been possible without the willingness to let go and detach from outcomes.

Letting it be means we aren't forcing ourselves to adopt a specific plan for our lives and that by letting it be we are *allowing* versus *forcing*. Allowing options to remain, letting go of timelines, and embracing the dangling of any loose ends.

I have learned that it can become apparent at any moment within our lives that another path is calling or meant for us. By clinging to old stories, scenarios, or the way we wish things had played out, we sometimes are being asked to pause within our story and say, "Okay, I'm listening. I'm allowing this change to be exactly as it is."

But I get it. This is all easier said than done.

Let it go, relax, stop worrying about it, chill out. You have probably heard these terms so many times. Being someone who has struggled with anxiety and perfectionism throughout my existence, I can't even begin to tell you how many times

I have been told to "just relax." In those moments, I have wanted to scream back, "How?"

It's never truly about the how. It is more about the *why.*

Letting it be is vital to our soul. By giving up the controlling aspects of our lives, we give ourselves room to live more freely and in the present moment.

HOW TO LET GO

Here are some ways to bring yourself back into your body and out of your thinking mind each time you find yourself obsessing over details, outcomes and what I call "future tripping," which means you are completely stuck on the grand finale of an outcome.

When your brain begins to wander off into a direction of overthinking, simply catch yourself and gently bring yourself back.

Don't entertain the idea, just accept the thought and remind yourself your thoughts will rarely create the existence you think they will.

When your mind suddenly fixates on a certain outcome or worry, remind yourself that this possibility is not the only outcome. There are limitless options available to us at all times. Make a list of all your thoughts from that day or week and write down or think about how many played out. Most times, what we think may happen never does.

As an example, when I first became ill, I was terrified to let my employer know that I was physically unable to work in the office. I would create so many scenarios around thinking they wouldn't accept my diagnosis or what I needed to heal. I would worry I would lose my income and go down spirals of negative thinking. It would keep me up at night, and it never allowed my body room to heal as it continuously activated my nervous system and caused anxiety. The truth is my employer was more accommodating and accepting than I could have ever imagine. The worries and the conscious choice of not letting it be created unnecessary anxiety in my body that only made me feel worse.

I did not realize I had a choice to change the thought pattern and fully stand in acceptance of what was.

Whatever it is that is stalking your thoughts right now, let it be. It doesn't matter, it never did, and your thoughts do nothing but instigate your emotions and delude you into thinking you can do something about it and control outcomes. Trust, release, let it go, exist minute by minute, and let all else drop away. Then pay close attention to how that feels in your body.

You are going to be okay. And you are safe.

This practice of letting it be and allowing led me to understand the depths of my personal need for feeling free as one of my core values is freedom. The more I began to practice this way of being the more I became drawn to letting go of *objects* within my physical possession and surroundings and adopt the idea of living minimally. The closet full of clothes you aren't wearing, a garage overflowing with things that you haven't used in years, a crappy relationship, a bad habit—they are all clutter.

While it seems it took a personal health crisis and a pandemic for me to finally embrace the freedom in letting it all be, I slowly began to step into who I have always known myself to be: someone who deeply values the importance of living an intentional, honest, and fully aligned life, so much so that within one year of living on my own I suddenly found myself roaming around my home making lists of what to sell, donate, and keep. I was asking myself what adds value and meaning to my life and what I could simply let go of.

I felt that if I was going to begin thinking in a new way and letting it all be, I would have to more importantly be an embodiment of that message. The embodying of the message is the action that comes from the belief within your mind. It is where the change begins to play out, and the outcomes truly begin to be witnessed. By letting go of most of physical possessions, I was then able to truly buy myself the time and space to focus on the life I was crafting for myself: one fully aligned with my core values and beliefs and one that had freedom at the top of that list.

Within one month, I reduced over half of my possessions, and it felt amazing. I'm not saying this level of decluttering is for everyone, but just the act of considering the process is enough to create a feeling of lightness in the body.

Truthfully, I was never comfortable in cluttered environments. It was always a struggle for me as a child to not start cleaning things up in other people's houses. It was an instinct I had to just want to clear piles off kitchen counters and clean out a closet. I always have had the ability to zone in on how I feel in an uncluttered space. You know that Wonder Woman feeling you get when your house is in order? That feeling.

What if for a moment you were to contemplate that your home reflects the way you view yourself and your thoughts? One of self-love, self-care, and joy. By celebrating your surroundings, you are truly celebrating yourself. By adopting a mindset of letting it be, allowing, and living for the moment, you are also embodying that message when you being to let go of physical objects that no longer serve a purpose in your life, using your surroundings as a doorway to health, wellness, vitality, and most importantly peace.

Clutter isn't just the stuff on your floor, it's anything that stands between you and the life you want to be living.

Let those words sink in for a moment. Ask yourself where holding onto items within your home even your work space has contributed to a feeling of overwhelm or anxiety. Consider how letting go of what is in your physical environment can then open up space and energy for the things you love.

Does your stuff and the things around you represent who you are today in this moment? Or who you were in the past?

To me it always was and still is about thinking to myself, *I want to wake up in the morning and feel like I can enjoy the day because I enjoy my space.* There is a powerful connection to the spaces we live and work in and what's happening in your head.

LETTING GO OF PERFECT TIMING

Over a decade ago I started a (very) part-time professional organizing business. It was on a whim from a friend who motivated me to take a chance on dabbling in what I love, taking cluttered spaces and making them simplified and aesthetically pleasing. I let go of any expectations around needing the timing to be perfect, having the perfect website, or having any credentials to speak of aside from this passion I had for organization. I posted a few pictures on Facebook of my sister's closet I had organized, set up a website, and because of the power of the share button the phone started to ring. Letting go of the need for everything to be perfect before making this choice led to an incredible career in professional organizing, one that I still am working in.

I vividly remember one client who was chronically ill that had asked me to help declutter her home. Because of the state of her health and living alone, her physical limitations caused her home to become extremely cluttered. In one of the rooms I was working in I found paintings she had painted herself buried in a closet. The images were stunning: gorgeous landscapes of oceans, mountains, and woods, all layered with beautiful colors. My heart sank at the idea these were hidden away and could bring her so much joy. I immediately removed them carefully, dusted them off, and displayed them on the walls in that room.

Within one month I returned for a follow-up to find her face looking brighter, her energy having shifted to a positive and peaceful demeanor. And she was painting again.

I know for sure what clutter and holding onto items we don't love is doing to us and why I believe it's time to turn it around: to take back our space, our thoughts, and the parts of our lives we have lost to clutter so we can surround ourselves with what we love.

IT'S WASTING OUR TIME

Clutter in every sense of the word is a time waster. You can't find your keys because they are buried under yesterday's mail. You can't find that thing that you know you put down right over there next to that other thing because there is so much stuff piled up on the counter. It's taking us longer to clean the house because of all the items we have to maneuver around and the items that need to be picked up. Last time I checked, time is kind of precious. It's actually all we have. So why are we wasting it looking for our stuff? Remember that we get to decide what comes in and goes out. It's your home, your space. Take back the clock and start to declutter day by day.

IT'S TAKING AWAY OUR ENERGY

Clutter is exhausting us whether we realize it or not. It's physically zapping us of our energy. We are in the habit of accumulating things but we are not in the habit of decluttering and purging. The more we accumulate, the less space there is for energy to flow, creating blocks all over our homes. Those blocks are messing with us. They are telling our brains we are overwhelmed and tired. This combination leads to stress and aggravation. You know the saying "home sweet home"? Let's take it literally and make our home sweet. Cookies and chocolate cake kind of sweet. I'd rather associate my home with feelings of dessert than piles of crappy unused items.

IT'S PREVENTING US FROM MAKING DECISIONS

Clutter is nothing more than postponed decisions. You put that there because it was the closest place to put it, not always the most logical or correct spot. Maybe everyone in your household does that too. Sometimes postponed decisions are just everywhere. This pattern keeps us from dealing with where to place things immediately and forces us to place them anywhere. This can start to carry out in our everyday lives as well. Taking a few minutes to mindfully places things in a spot that you decided is best for that item to live, and keeping like items together will save you time and energy in the long run.

I can say with certainty our homes will never be picture perfect. To be honest, Pinterest sort of makes me crazy with all the images it shows of these perfectly kept homes. While perfectionism is not realistic, giving ourselves the opportunity to enjoy our time, feel good, and make decisions with ease certainly is. So let's start to take our homes back. One decision at a time.

When I became sick, everything stopped and then the world stopped. The stillness is where I found myself again, and with that came the realization that in order to move forward and step into the life that is fully aligned with my purpose, my vision, and my values, it would require a short-term action plan for my long-term vision.

There are days I wish I could live unattached, distracted, and unaware of the importance of a life lived rooted deeply in our truth. But the truth is that is no longer possible for me. The practice and act of choosing to let it be in each moment brings me back to the present moment.

FAVORITE MINIMALIST MANTRAS

Freedom exists within living out my values and my truth, not acquiring more to distract from my path.
Less, but better.
The less you own, the less that owns you.
Once we give up being attached to the physical possessions, we find the time and freedom to follow our biggest dreams.
Lightness over Heaviness
Clarity over Clutter
Space over Confinement
Gratitude over Unappreciation
Flow over Stagnancy
Freedom over Difficulty
Inspiration over Demotivation
Growth over Regression

Maybe right now is the perfect time to let go, to let it be. What is the worst that could happen?

I think the question is what is the *best* that could happen? The only person you can give permission to let go is you. May you find your own path to simplicity, intentional living, and a life lived on your terms.

A SPACE FOR JOURNALING AND REFLECTION.

A SPACE FOR JOURNALING AND REFLECTION.

CHAPTER 10

"You deserve to be completely found in your surroundings, not lost within them."

RUPI KAUR

There is a depth of mystery in the natural world. The incredible healing, restorative, and peaceful power of nature has dramatic effects on our well-being. Nature has provided me relief during some of the most trying times in my life: divorce, death, and illness. It calms my nervous system, keeps me present, and creates gratitude for the simplest of things.

Everything in nature has a purpose, a cycle, and a flow that happens so effortlessly and in sync. There is an ebb and flow, like a season change. Our bodies respond to this natural rhythm and flow. In 1984, E.O. Wilson introduced and popularized the term "biophilia." He defined this idea as "the connections that human beings subconsciously seek with the rest of life." There is a strong intuitive link between nature and our well-being.

Repeatedly, studies have found that people have a strong preference for natural settings over man-made environments across all cultures. This suggests, along with Wilson's biophilia hypothesis, that our preferences are an evolutionary response.

What would feel more calming to you after a long workweek: a weekend spent quietly in nature with a gorgeous landscape or a view of the ocean, or a crowded city with nowhere to relax? I think you may respond strongly to the prospect of refuge.

I like to think of nature as magic.

At the beginning of 2019, I had made a commitment to hike every weekend for the entire year, a total of fifty-two hikes. It was mostly due to past overachieving ways and maybe more of a subconscious craving of nature. Call it instinct. I didn't quite make the goal, but the effort allowed me to spend over half the year, through each season, immersed in nature.

I hiked in seven states. I wandered up mountains, sitting at the top in awe at the landscape below me. I spent time in deserts, looking up at the brightest night sky and feeling small and powerless in comparison to what appeared infinite above me. I hiked alongside the ocean, watching the waves roll in and the sunset lighting up the water. I spent time deep in the woods, where the only sounds you hear are the birds and the leaves rustling in the wind. This experience far surpassed anything material I could have gifted myself. It tested my strength, mentally and physically. It was conscious effort and free will.

One hiking trip specifically changed my perspective on the power of nature so profoundly that I don't believe I can ever go longer than a month without immersing myself in nature somehow.

I had planned a solo trip to Sedona, as I heard some inspiring transformative stories about the spiritual and sacred aspect of this town, notably what is known as the Sedona vortex. According to the Visit Sedona website, vortexes (the proper grammatical form "vortices" is rarely used) are thought to be swirling centers of energy that are conducive to healing, meditation, and self-exploration. These are places where the earth seems especially alive with energy. Many people feel inspired, recharged, or uplifted after visiting a vortex.

I flew into Phoenix and made the drive from the airport to Sedona and knew the moment I approached the sunset gleaming off the red rock mountains this would be one of the most magical places I had ever seen.

As I approached my Airbnb, I was having some trouble finding it and parked my rental car in the neighborhood where I was staying. I decided to travel on foot to search for the house number since it was beginning to get dark and felt like I'd have more luck on foot.

"Are you lost, love?"

The irony of this question that was coming from a stranger's voice behind me has never been lost on me. I think one of the biggest reasons for my trip out to this magical place was fueled by the always present feeling of "being lost." I was somehow being drawn to nature as a healer yet didn't realize it at the time.

I chuckled to myself and turned around to find an older woman behind me walking her adorable black lab. She clearly noticed my wandering in this small neighborhood nestled within the red rock mountains of Sedona, where I was certain everyone knew each other.

"I am. I'm trying to find number 110."

"Oh, let me walk you there. Follow me."

I followed this lovely stranger, awkwardly pulling along my carry-on and lugging my backpack, wondering how long she'd been watching me walking in circles. I'm not the best at small talk. In fact, I'm terrible at it. I glow and expand in deep conversation, layered with honesty as people reveal who they are. I seem to shrink when prompted to search for a conversation starter. I did feel the need, however, to say something to break the silence as the only sound was my carry-on being dragged over the pavement.

"I'm Lauren, by the way. I'm from Rhode Island. It's beautiful there, mostly in the summers but *not* in the winters. This is a different kind of beauty here in Sedona." It came out of my mouth like one run-on sentence. I made it obvious how uncomfortable I can be with new acquaintances.

She looked over at me and smiled as if to say, "Yes, I am aware."

"Here we are, number 110. Enjoy your stay here."

"Thank you so much. So nice of you to help a lost traveler."

As she started to walk away, she turned around and gave her dog a good rub on the back, and then said with confidence, "Sometimes we need to get lost to find our way. I'm Emily by the way. Welcome to Sedona."

The tears started to well up. I stood there in the dark, tired from a day of travel, in my wrinkled clothes with a growling belly. Emily was the name of my grandmother. She had passed just seven months prior to my trip. I missed her dearly. She was the matriarch of my family with a laugh that would light up a room. She loved hard with an intensity that made anyone who was in her presence feel loved, seen, and heard. Hearing her name from the mouth of this incredibly kind stranger, who was offering words of wisdom at a time when I may have been the most lost I had ever been in my life, moved me. In that moment I knew I was in the right place. Lost, but in the right place.

The next morning, I woke up and landed on the trails at dawn. About an hour into a solo hike, I had not seen another human. It was complete solitude among some of the most beautiful red rock mountains. My feet sank slowly into the ground with each step. The ground resembled a soft red clay after the prior evening's passing shower. I hiked through Cathedral Rock, and as I neared the end of the steady length of the trail, I made my way past a rocky staircase. After a few switchbacks past a juniper tree, a sign at the top labeled "End of Trail" greeted me between the two walls of the Cathedral Rock formation. The view over the edge was one of the most amazing sites. The sun had just made its way through the clouds and lit up the mountains in the distance with colors of bright red and browns, making the sky appear an incredibly vibrant blue. I sat there in awe, taking in the beauty and feeling one of the most peaceful waves of energy pass over me.

That trip taught me how to listen when it's quiet rather than needing to speak over the silence. It also taught me how incredibly healing this earth can be. I left there with a renewed sense of gratitude and love for our planet.

And that gratitude was what I reached into during my healing from chronic illness. It was what I reconnected to and needed most. Nature became one of the biggest parts of my healing. At the time I did not realize how important this lesson was.

There was a study done in the 1980s at a hospital in Paoli, a small town in Pennsylvania. The researcher who conducted the study wanted to understand the factors involved in a patient's recovery time when healing. It seemed some of the hospital beds faced a brick wall, while others had a view of trees. The patients who had beds facing the brick wall had longer recovery times and felt generally depressed, while those with beds facing the trees healed much faster. Nature had an overall positive effect on how quickly their bodies responded to healing.

What you are seeing, hearing, and experiencing at any moment is changing not only your mood, but how your nervous, endocrine, and immune systems are working.

The stress of an unpleasant environment can cause you to feel anxious, sad, or helpless. This in turn elevates your blood pressure, heart rate, and muscle tension and suppresses your immune system. A pleasing environment reverses that. Once the body has received messages of calm, peace, and ease, it can relax.

When I first learned of the practice of grounding, or "earthing," as some refer to it, it was mid-March in the

Northeast, and the ground was still thawing from the winter. Grounding is the practice of going barefoot on the ground, sitting, standing, or even walking. I knew I had to wait a bit before I could get my feet comfortably bare on the ground, so I just began sitting outside in the mornings with a hot cup of tea and a pair of very warm socks.

The earth is essentially a giant battery that contains a natural, subtle electrical charge. It's an incredibly unique and special energy that is present in the ground. Mostly everything in the electrical world is connected to it. That's what the term "grounded" means. Whether you knew this or not, trust me. I was very new to this information myself. You are a bioelectrical being living on an electrical planet. All your cells transmit multiple frequencies that run our heart, nervous system, and immune system.

Yet as an industrialized and civilized society, you have been wearing shoes for quite a while. We all have. Walking into work barefoot probably wouldn't go over well with the boss. This has acted as a barrier to the earth's energy. So, we all have become "disconnected" and ungrounded.

I knew within the first week of beginning the first twenty minutes of my day that this exercise was having an impact on my health. And I related the grounding back to what I experienced at Cathedral Rock in Sedona.

I practiced this grounding exercise for months. Every morning I would make some tea, sit outside, take my shoes off, bury my feet into the earth, close my eyes, and just breathe. I did this before opening an email or checking social media. It became a morning ritual I could not skip.

If you have experienced chronic illness, you may know mornings can be the most difficult time of the day as you can feel exhausted despite having slept an entire night. That feeling of being ready to jump out of bed and start the day was something I had missed terribly and struggled to regain for a long time. Having this morning ritual, however, gave me something to look forward to. And I slowly found my body responding to this exercise and waking up became a little easier as each day went by.

In a study done by PubMed Central, it was found that through grounding, the natural defenses of the body can be restored. Further research expands on this idea, and it supports the practice of grounding as improving our health and well-being exponentially through decreasing levels of inflammation and pain, stress reduction, and mood improvement. It helps to improve chronic fatigue, chronic pain, inflammation, and sleep disorders.

Besides taking your shoes off and allowing your feet to touch the earth, you can also lie on the ground or swim in the ocean or a lake.

I don't believe you have to be on the brink of burnout or exhaustion or fully immersed in it as I was to begin to appreciate and want to use nature as a healer. You may find yourself having little time for you and your soul and in need of some self-care.

Ask yourself the last time you spent an hour in nature, without your cell phone, without distraction. And ask yourself if your wellness is worth the effort to try.

When you learn about yourself in calming environments, you begin to know when to slow down and when to act. From a calm, centered, and grounded position, you can make decisions that are right for you to feel more present in each moment and generally excited about life. When you are acting from this position, you are more likely to experience peace, stability, joy, and overall health.

EIGHT WAYS NATURE HEALED ME

It inspired creativity and boosted my brain cells.

It deepened my spiritual growth and practice.

It allowed me to choose healthier habits.

It drew past trauma and habits not serving me to the surface and gave them a chance to be brought to light and healed.

It balanced my central nervous system.

It cleared out old and stagnant emotions.

It allowed me to breathe deeper.

It allowed me to look up.

Are you convinced to take this step and invite more of the natural elements into your life to promote growth, healing, and peace?

There are times it may take aloneness to learn the things that make you come alive. Allow your body to breathe again and fully heal. It may take a walk on the beach with nothing but your thoughts or a simple walk through a park. It might look like getting on a plane and flying across the country to land in a new town and explore the new landscape around you. Or it could just mean stepping outside your own door and sitting quietly in your backyard.

Whatever that might look like to you, follow it. Follow that call to nature when it arrives and stay present in its asking.

"I went to the woods because I wished to live deliberately, to front only the essential facts of life, and see if I could not learn what it had to teach, and not, when I came to die, discover that I had not lived."—Henry David Thoreau

A SPACE FOR JOURNALING AND REFLECTION.

A SPACE FOR JOURNALING AND REFLECTION.

CHAPTER 11

"To a mind that is still, a whole universe surrenders."

LAO TZU

It was a cold Northeast winter in 2019 when I flew out to California to visit my cousin. Every time I head out to the southern California desert a certain refuge and calm wash over me. The desert sunsets take over her property with the most incredible hues of pink, purple, and orange that form just over the hills in the distance. I stare up into the desert sky at night in awe of the sky's vastness hovering over me. Wandering through Joshua Tree National Park with my favorite playlist and chasing the wildflowers that bloom across an otherwise barren landscape has always quieted any storm that I felt brewing in my mind.

Home feels incredibly far away: far away from the lowland forests and rocky storm-wracked coasts, the dominance of white and gray colors covering the landscape in the Northeast winter. Yet with that feeling comes a strong sense of belonging and peace. There is something meditative and calming about this part of the desert that makes me come alive. This desert that taught me the power of meditation and the peace and happiness that come from clearing your mind. And I also realized it was something I could access within me anytime, anywhere. It all happened lying down inside a thirty-eight-foot high, fifty-five-foot wide wooden dome called the Integratron.

The Integratron in Landers, California, sits twenty miles north of Joshua Tree National Park, in the middle of the Mojave Desert. In the about section on the property's website it explains it was built in 1958 by George Van Tassel, an aeronautical engineer, author, and inventor. The location is essential to its functioning. It was built on an intersection of strong geomagnetic forces that amplify the Earth's magnetic field. It offers a sound bath complete with thirty-five minutes of twenty quartz crystal singing bowls played live. As you lie down in the dome during the sound bath in a multiwave sound chamber, a sequence of quartz crystal singing bowls are played. Each bowl is keyed to the energy centers or chakras of the body where sound becomes medicine for the nervous system. The results are waves of peace, heightened awareness, and a total relaxation of the mind and body.

I entered that dome and walked the steps up toward the space where the sound bath was given, thousands of miles from home. Lying there on the floor among strangers and completely open and accepting of the experience was when I learned how to meditate. I let the music move through me and focused on the experience, allowing myself to become completely present. Any physical sensations of pain, worry, or anxiety over the future seemed to dissipate. I was completely living in the present moment.

And isn't that truly all we have? The present moment.

"Sound therapy is deeply rooted in science and based on the principles of quantum physics and sacred geometry. There are hundreds of clinical trials and peer-reviewed white paper studies on the healing properties of sound," says Christina Resasco, a sound healing practitioner and yoga therapist at Saffron & Sage in San Diego, California.

Prior to visiting this magical place out in the Mojave, I had dabbled in meditation. After a long day I would sit crossed-legged on the floor with my eyes closed and put on some soothing music. If I sat for ten minutes at least eight of those minutes were filled with my mind flying in a million directions and my own inner voice trying to get myself to come back to center. Suddenly checklists of things I could be doing and random thoughts in that moment would begin to pop up in my mind.

The dialogue in my mind would play out something like this:

I think I'm about to run out of almond milk. I should probably go get some.

You're meditating right now, Lauren. It can wait.

I wonder why that customer at work is so passive aggressive over email. I think she hates me.

Not a valid thought right now, Lauren. You're too mindful to worry about what other people think. Remember, you're a meditator.

Am I really, though? Because I'm pretty sure I'm just sitting here with my eyes closed and now I'd like a nap.

But I kept trying despite the thoughts. So, I then moved onto guided meditations. These seemed to help me concentrate a bit more and tune into the person's voice as they helped redirect my brain to the present moment, but I saved those only for when I felt anxious or scattered and noticed a high level of stress in my body. What I was missing, however, was the whole *point* of meditation.

The point of meditating, regardless of where or how you decide to do it, is to literally carve out space between external environmental stimulus and your response—between your thoughts and action. It is essentially a form of exercise for the mind. And just as you would train your body to run your first five-kilometer race, training your mind to simply accept a thought and allow it to move through you is the same concept.

And you don't need to fly out to the California desert to become an expert in or even experience the benefits of meditation.

One of the things I love most about embracing meditation is it can be accessed at any time in our day and shift our energy within minutes. Think of the times within your life that you could most benefit from this practice. Many of us may think we don't have enough time in our day to commit to taking the time to sit with ourselves and quiet the mind. But taking the time to reconnect with ourselves far outweighs the price we sometimes pay for not honoring our inner stillness.

> *"Within you there is a stillness and*
> *sanctuary to which you can retreat*
> *at any time and be yourself."*
>
> ***HERMANN HESSE***

Visit this space often, even in the times that you resist. In the times we resist, the practice is most needed.

Meditation for me became a daily practice when I was moving through my healing journey. Living in a state of chronic pain with exceptionally low levels of energy affected my mood in ways I had never experienced. My once-vibrant self became withdrawn and moody. I felt disconnected from myself and knew this was perpetuating my illness. I became committed to a meditation practice, knowing instinctively it would somehow lift my spirits, if only for a few moments a day.

Meditation allowed me the space to quiet my mind and stop fixating on the pain in body and the fatigue that at times seemed overwhelming. The most important factor was it continuously calmed my nervous system so my body could access a healing state. It helped me respond to the world and daily stressors from a place of a reflection and curiosity, versus reactivity and defensiveness.

You deserve to feel calm and supported in your body and free from a constant feeling of stress.

Every morning before I start my day, I take ten minutes to settle in, take three deep inhales and exhales, and listen to a recorded meditation. One of my favorites is on the *Live Awake* podcast, from Sarah Blondin. Her words help to bring me back to center and ground me for the day. Regardless of what is happening around me, it helps to realign and center me.

Over time, this practice has helped to keep my body within a healing state, and I truly believe my meditation practice is one of the reasons I was able to recover from unease.

> *"You will learn that the true purpose of meditation is to get beyond the analytical mind and enter into the subconscious mind so you can make real and permanent changes. If you get up from meditation as the same person who sat down, nothing has happened to you on any level."*
>
> DR. JOE DISPENZA

WHY AND HOW MEDITATION HEALS

It calms chaos and scattered thinking.

Regular meditation releases dopamine and serotonin (the happy hormone) in the body, which reduces the release of stress hormones and maintains your calmness. Frequent releases of these endorphins regulate your mood, creating a more balanced level of being.

As your mind becomes balanced, brain synchronization occurs. This opens the door to even more benefits such as easier learning, better mental health, and super creativity.

The simple act of closing our eyes, shifting our focus inward, and removing all the clutter and daily worries from the mind can light up dormant cells of our brain that are not usually activated when we are in a state of stress.

It relieves anxiety.

Anxiety is essentially worry about the future or past, keeping us in a state of feeling unable to move forward as we are so fixated on what-if or what-was. Daily meditation helps you acknowledge and comprehend your thoughts and emotions better, which keeps you focused on the present moment.

Anxiety, worry, and fear cannot exist in the present moment. There is no running toward an outcome or thinking back on what could have been. There is only the moment you have. Being present also guarantees a happier life experience as we focus on what is happening in and around us.

It helps us gain clarity on the future.

Daily meditation allows you to listen to your inner self. When your inner self is awakened, you become more intuitive.

In a study led by Wake Forest University, researchers observed the brains of fifteen volunteers before and after four days of mindfulness training. In addition to a host of other brain enhancements, the meditators increased the activity and interconnectivity in their prefrontal cortex, which is the axis of intuition. What does this mean for you and me? Daily meditation hits the switch on our brain's axis and links us directly to our ultrapowerful sense of inner knowing.

It helps us find solutions.

Have you ever felt off about something or someone, yet ignored the emotional response your body was sending? Next time this happens, I invite you to meditate on it, to tap into your inner knowing.

One of the most powerful meditations I have used that I learned through spiritual teacher, leader, and author Gabby

Bernstein prompts us to tap into our intuitive mind to find the answers that are already living within us.

Whenever I am sitting in confusion in my life, I sit in silence and say the below mantra that Gabby teaches in her spirit guide meditation. Within minutes, the answers usually come to me from a place of clear understanding and knowing.

"Thank you, guides of the highest truth and compassion. Thank you for showing me what I need to know. Thank you for leading me in the right direction. Thank you for whatever it is that I need."

These guides live within each of us, and we can access them when needed.

It heals.

It is scientifically proven that a body living with a constant state of anxiety cannot heal. When your body has an overabundance of cortisol, the high levels interfere with the production of anti-inflammatory substances called cytokines. The result is a constant inflammatory response, which makes it extremely hard for our bodies to get into a healing state.

The calmer we are, the happier our insides are.

It's my intention that you can fully embrace the idea of meditation and incorporate it into your life.

You can use meditation to send out love to others, to heal past traumas, to find answers to the burning questions, or to simply clear your mind. You can use it to show up in this world with a loving presence.

To live a heart-centered life, we must become still and listen.

Right now, as you are reading this, take a moment to sit back, take a long inhale, hold for two seconds, then let it out for six seconds. This breath work immediately relaxes the vagus nerve, which is the nerve in your body that triggers your body's relaxation response. It instantly lowers the body's stress response. Once you feel your body relax, take a moment to close your eyes and just sit in silence. If thoughts appear, let them. Don't judge them, force them away, or start a dialogue with them. Simply accept the thought and then move on. Try this for a minute or two, and then come back to this chapter, because I think you will want to know what happens within our body during meditation beyond quieting our stress response.

Feeling better? A bit more relaxed? I hope so. Keep trying this daily and take note of any shifts in your mood and energy. Just by taking a deep inhale and exhale, you are sending important messages to your brain to fall into a more relaxed state.

A SPACE FOR JOURNALING AND REFLECTION.

A SPACE FOR JOURNALING AND REFLECTION.

"A TESTAMENT TO THE POWER OF MEDITATION"

FROM JOANNA E. READ

My journey into meditation has been an ever-evolving exploration into remembering, reclaiming, and rebirthing my embodied, sovereign wholeness. It has been one of humility, perseverance, acceptance, grace, trust, healing, liberation, wonder, awe, and allowing the parts of me that have been buried, shamed, suppressed, or denied, to be excavated, illuminated, and compassionately integrated, breath by breath, moment by moment, in small, incremental steps (often quite circuitously.)

While much of my life has revolved around contemplative practices such as yoga, art, expressive writing, athletics, and connection with nature, each modality enriching and complementing one another in greater levels of expression, it wasn't until a series of destabilizing events in early 2020 that I realized something critical was missing in my foundation.

Meditation illuminated what was missing, and at the same time, it led me to realize nothing had ever been lost to begin with. Little by little, meditation became a framework for navigating day-to-day life with greater awareness, connection, and attunement to my thoughts, feelings, and, ultimately, the innate intelligence of my body, the wisdom of my soul, and the greater world around me.

I wish I could say this was a quick and easy fix, that the more fruitful aspects of my practice (enriching creativity, deepening fulfillment, and establishing a felt sense of belonging, connection, safety, and trust in the universe at large) came to me immediately. The reality is for many months, it seemed as though not much was happening, other than meeting my own humility around such a seemingly "simple" task feeling *so* frustrating, even pointless. Yet, at the same time, I was also beginning to experience little moments of grace and reprise, which gradually began to sprout tiny roots, as the seed of my intention to liberate my mind and body began to crack open in the cool, fertile darkness of the earth.

When I finally made the choice to commit to developing a consistent mindfulness-based stress reduction practice (which has since evolved and expanded into other forms and styles of meditation, yet remains an anchoring practice), it didn't take long for the root of my very resistance to meditation to be brought to light.

Only through slowing down and being still did I come to realize I had been holding an innate fear of *doing nothing.* This fear spoke as a visceral sense in my nervous system of feeling as though the floor beneath me would collapse if I remained still for longer than ten minutes. It was as though my body was saying, "If you stop moving, you won't be able to survive."

In other words, my mind and nervous system had created a story that said in order to be safe, I needed to be a human *doing*, not a human *being*.

Not until I actually sat myself down did I realize how I had, in a sense, been unconsciously treading water in the river of survival for most of my life. Yet, as I continued to show up and practice, the fear and anxiety I felt in my body began to slowly dissolve. The fleeting moments of grace, stillness, and reprise began to gather little by little, weaving into a raft that gently supported me in navigating what I learned was actually a river of change. In this undulating stream of unknowing I found myself within, the bank of my old ways of being had collapsed, yet I couldn't quite tell who the new "self" was on the other side of the shore.

Meditation provided a consistent structure and felt sense of support and safety within these liminal waters, offering space for the deep rest and repair that was needed in my mind, heart, and nervous system. Meditation, along with self-directed expressive arts therapies, coaching, and journaling became my foundation for integrative healing.

Little did I know my fear of doing nothing was only the tip of the iceberg. Life events in the next eighteen months would lead me deep into the underworld of the psyche. As I developed consistency with my practice, mediation became my training ground in the art of discernment as I met these shadow aspects: teaching me how to witness the messy, ugly, and painful thoughts and feelings that were coming up to the surface, without identifying *as* these thoughts any longer. This was a newfound liberation.

I knew from studying the work of Dr. Joe Dispenza my commitment to this practice wasn't fluff or magical thinking—it was, in fact, healing and rewiring my brain, body, and nervous system on a cellular level. I also knew from the research that, in the initial stages of practice, my brain and body would likely put up a fight and want to kick back, because of how entrained my mind had become to certain debilitating, unconscious habits and thought patterns, each of which producing a corresponding emotion with a chemical response—stress hormones like cortisol and adrenaline that were slowly eroding not only my mental and emotional well-being, but also impacting all systems of my physical body. These stress hormones, and even the stressful thoughts themselves, I learned, my brain had actually grown to *crave* from their very familiarity.

I braced myself for the pushback and committed. I knew if I could condition my physical body to climb a rope, do a pull-up, backpack in the wilderness, and scale rock walls, I could also condition my mind and body to, eventually, settle down. Through applying a similar process of steady, incremental practice through focus, attention, and repetition, I'd experience progress.

The tricky part with this was my mind was so conditioned to "performing" that, to apply the same principle, without trying to control or direct the outcome, "achieve" anything in particular, or "get it right," all felt entirely disorienting. Like most people, the very concept was a whole new paradigm for my brain: it didn't have any embodied context for it, and it was deeply imprinted in my ancestral roots.

True to my hypothesis, as I committed to my practice and developed consistency to the best of my ability, my capacity to focus my mind and my stamina for sitting in silence with myself increased. The floor beneath me no longer felt as though it was collapsing. I began to feel anchored and rooted in my body, strong in my spine, and soft in my skin, belly, and eventually, in my heart. My sits became longer. I was starting to trust life.

I added in walking meditations to my routine: engaging all of my senses on slow, methodical walks, feeling my feet connect with the soft earth, embracing the gifts of nature's sights, smells, sounds, tastes, and felt sensations. I'd also practice walking "Dispenza style"—embodying new energetic signatures of empowered thoughts and feelings, *walking as confidence*, for example, feeling the frequency of these thoughts in my body, emanating it, and all the while tracking my thoughts and somatic experience with greater awareness.

To this day, I'm continually learning and evolving in my ability to stay present and attuned with my mind and body. When the dark thoughts of fear, shame, or inadequacy arise, I do the best I can to meet them, as opposed to automatically rejecting, dismissing, or reacting to them. While I'm far from perfect with any of this, meditation has greatly enhanced my ability to catch myself in high-intensity moments and more quickly pause, breathe, and respond from a regulated state rather than reactivity.

The beautiful paradox within this journey has been that, while my initial drive to devote myself to a practice sought to "fix" or "resolve" what I felt was *missing*, the practice itself actually led me to realize I was seeking was wholeness, and it had existed within me all along. It had simply become buried from years of counterconditioning, not only from my personal lifetime but from the accumulation of conditioning of many generations past.

Not until I committed to a meditation practice did I realize no amount of reading about wholeness could ever substitute for the somatic experience of *feeling* this grace and expansion within my body, and, again, it took a lot of time, commitment, and effort to start getting tastes of it. I share this to say, stick with it! Once you develop some consistency, you'll start experiencing results. Eventually, you may find yourself becoming inspired to show up for your practice, because you're seeing how your inner and outer worlds are evolving and growing and bringing you closer to your dreams. For those of you reading who are new to meditation or perhaps coming back to your practice after some time away: you've got this. I believe in you. If you want, you can even start, right now.

Become aware of your body's connection with whatever you are sitting or lying upon. Notice if you're holding any tension in your scalp, brow, jaw, shoulders, chest, or belly. Sense into the quality of your breath as it travels in and out of your lungs. Allow your inhales to feel gentle and soft, your exhales washing through your body like a warm, cleansing waterfall. Let your eyelids become heavy and allow your gaze to soften, or even close your eyes. After some time, gently begin to deepen your breathing a bit more without forcing anything. See if you can let your belly soften a bit, and allow your low ribs to expand a little on the inhale. This is called diaphragmatic breathing, which helps to activate the "rest and digest" aspect of your nervous system. You might even try counting in for a count of five on the inhale and exhaling for a count of seven. This is called heart resonance breathing, and counting can sometimes be a helpful way to focus the mind a bit more. Notice how it feels in your body to breathe in this way.

Now, notice how natural it is for your mind to wander off in thoughts. For this practice, we aren't trying to get rid of the thoughts. We're simply allowing them to pass by without grabbing onto them or creating stories around them. You might find it helpful to think of your thoughts like birds in the sky: we aren't trying to catch or fly off with the birds . . . we're simply allowing them to be as they are as we practice remaining present with our gentle inhales and exhales. When you notice you've wandered off in a thought or a story, that's a good thing! The fact you noticed the drifting away is building new neural pathways—kind of like every time you bring yourself back to the present moment is putting in a "rep" that's building a new "muscle" of resilience in your brain, in the same way you would practice putting in repetitions of air squats if you wanted to condition a stronger core and lower body. Continue to remain present to the best of your ability, and keep bringing yourself back again and again. There is no need to judge or criticize. Just keep coming back to your breathing, and keep letting those birds fly free. For the next few moments, or longer, simply allow this to be your practice, and let it be enough. And come back tomorrow and the next day!

With time, you'll realize how much it helps to be gentle and compassionate with yourself, especially when you're first starting out. After all, moving from being reflexive to being deliberate takes practice! Do the best you can to be kind to yourself as you learn and grow. Find a support system—a friend, therapist, coach, or group who can help you feel seen, encouraged, and inspired in your practice. You'll find as you learn to cultivate compassion and be kind to yourself in the mess and the muck, an interesting thing will start happening: you'll start to have more patience and empathy for others.

As the seeds of your initial practice gradually take root, sprout, and find their way into the light of the sun to bloom, you'll come to be inspired by the fruits of your practice, and you'll want to share the goodness with others. You'll see yourself in a new light with expanded potential. You'll remember your practice is not selfish, it's self-full . . . and your practice is not only for you, it's for your family, your loved ones, the people you work with, the person next to you in traffic. You'll remember your practice is for the world, because you'll feel the whole of the world within you. And in the moments when you forget, all you need to do is remember and begin again—breath by beautiful gift of breath.

Joanna E. Read,
Artist, Certified Professional Coach, Yoga Teacher
joannaread.com | joannaread.etsy.com | @joannaeread

A SPACE FOR JOURNALING AND REFLECTION.

A SPACE FOR JOURNALING AND REFLECTION.

CHAPTER 12

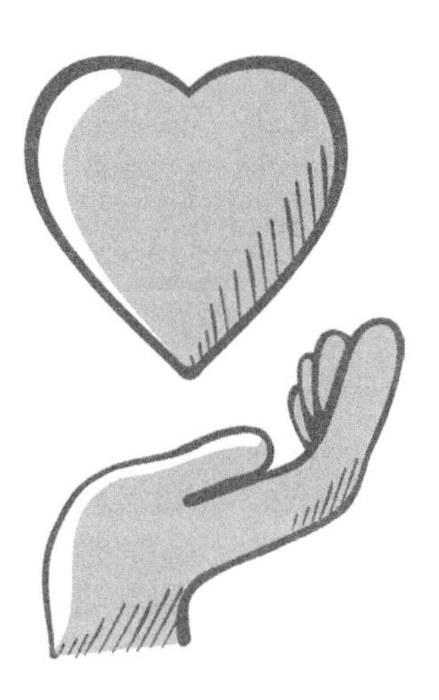

Love Yourself. Fully, Deeply, Honestly, Gloriously.

Would you like to hear an epic love story?

Once upon a time a girl loved herself so deeply that she checked in with herself every so often to ask: Are the relationships in my life bringing out the best in me or draining me of my precious energy? Am I honoring the gifts of deep and meaningful connections? Or am I forcing myself to connect with people who don't truly see me for who I am?

I learned to ask myself these questions when I was moving through my healing and began to learn more about how our bodies emotionally respond to interactions with others. I learned it is essential it is to our well-being to surround ourselves with others who are going to truly lift us higher, empower us, and hold up a mirror so we can turn inward to witness how we can show up better in the world. Throughout my healing journey, I had a very heightened state of awareness of how I was feeling in my body when I was interacting with others.

THE RELATIONSHIP TO SELF AND OTHERS

Relationships with others are one the most fascinating ways to learn about ourselves if we are committed to paying attention to how they are affecting our lives. Yet the relationship to self is the foundation for everything. We are either showing up in our relationships as the most authentic version of ourselves, or not honoring our own needs.

We embark on the journey of relationships to connect with others to help take on life's challenges with a helpful support system, for companionship, mutual respect, and feelings of safety. Whether these relationships are romantic or with friends or family I found that the basis for these to thrive was to intentionally rebuild the relationship I had with myself. To embark on the inner work.

As I began to heal my body I also began to heal the parts of me that had never truly felt aligned or safe in the relationships I had chosen. It was disheartening for me to uncover so many truths of how I was approaching the relationships in my life. How I hid my true feelings, withdrew myself when others opened up to me, yet moved in closer when they pushed back, and allowed real friendship to fall away.

Yet I wanted desperately to connect with others on a conscious and aligned level. But wasn't this happening?

At times what we are searching for from others is what we are absent in ourselves. This need I had for connection, to be understood, to be seen, was a call for me to find that within myself. This then eliminates the need to seek outside of ourselves.

Any good relationship requires balance, ease, grace, and paying attention to our own internal needs. When I started to become comfortable sitting in my own insecurity, my connections with others, and the understanding that much of what I was seeking in others I had to first find within me, I was able to filter through my relationships with others and begin to actively participate in how I felt.

Notice how you feel the next time you have a negative interaction with a coworker, family member, or a friend. Take a moment to check in with how your body feels. Is there a tightening in your chest? An uncomfortable feeling in your stomach? Do you suddenly feel drained after speaking to them? Are you showing up authentically or showing up as how you want them to perceive you?

Maybe there is a persistent feeling of disconnection or insecurity. It's as though you are putting in so much effort, yet they seem to withdraw feelings or not make an effort. Or maybe they are the ones who are making an effort to be present in your life, yet you withdraw from their invitation to connect.

These physical feelings, responses, and signs of imbalance can give us insight into our relationships with others, and more importantly how we can learn to move through the more difficult relationships, be it casual or formal, with ease and grace, from a place of self-love and safety. For me, it became an open invitation to understand how the dynamics of the relationships in my life were affecting my well-being, energy, and livelihood—how they were affecting my *health.*

There are those relationships we must maintain within our work environments and within our family that we can create boundaries around to protect our energy, and then there are those we consciously choose to invite into our lives. They are equally important and vital to our well-being.

Understanding how to navigate through these has been one of the biggest learning experiences of my life, especially because I identify so much as an introvert. Or, as I like to say, I'm naturally introverted and selectively extroverted.

For so long, I would gravitate toward others who would dominate our conversations, take the lead, be more comfortable controlling our surroundings, and not consider my needs. This relationship dynamic caused me to shrink rather than expand. I always justified it as, "Well, I'm naturally an introvert, so I need someone always in control." These different communication styles within relationship are okay in our lives and will always be present. It's naive to think we all grow up learning the exact same methods of communication, relationship dynamics, and ways to process emotion. It is certainly not healthy to only surround ourselves with people just like us.

What I failed to realize however is I was moving toward imbalanced relationships by hiding myself away which naturally causes, you guessed it, imbalance! I now understood the strong connection between relationships and health. I was consistently choosing imbalanced relationships that extended from job choices misaligned with my values, to failing to acknowledge my unique ways of communication in romantic partnerships, to friendships. And with not properly addressing family dynamics and how these relationships were playing out in my life, how could this not bear any weight on what was happening inside my body?

We cannot heal in the same way that caused us to be unwell, out of balance, and misaligned. Some view balance as a myth, or unachievable. I say it is essential to our health.

How can relationships thrive in the absence of it?

I am wildly talkative in the presence of those I am most comfortable with. Place me in a room full of strangers and I will find the one person I can connect with and talk to them for the remainder of my time there. I often worry my behavior comes across as aloof or rude but I think we are naturally drawn to what we are most comfortable with. I have come to learn that by embracing this side of me I am essentially honoring what I need. Yet there are times when socializing and stepping out of comfort zone to connect with others is needed and vital for growth and expansion. This is when understanding how to balance these dualities becomes an important tool for growth.

I don't believe I am shy, but rather a noticer. A thinker, an observer. I treasure my solitude and I don't enjoy small talk. I have a few close friends, and I appreciate the beauty of deep and true connection.

I didn't discover how much of an introvert I was until I reached my forties. I thought back to all the socializing I had done in my twenties, and even into my thirties, and how exhausted I would feel after a night out with a large group of friends. Or how I preferred to hide away in my room as a child, writing in my journal or playing quietly by myself in the backyard. Sure, I had many friends, but I always felt the most at ease around a small group.

I have always had deep admiration for those who maintain a large social circle well into their adult lives. A part of me has found it fascinating how some of us thrive in large groups, with a constantly packed calendar of parties, get-togethers, and invites. The girls who have a closet overflowing with bridesmaid's dresses for all the weddings they've been in, their social media photos filled with large groups of people.

For a very long time, I wanted to be that adult. The social butterfly. The one with the packed calendar, who was working the room in every party, chatting up strangers in elevators, and making connections like a boss.

When I first started my professional organizing business, I was told I should really get out to more networking events, so I would force myself to go to networking events and leave exhausted, unfulfilled, and feeling like a failure. I'd bring a stack of business cards with me and promise myself that I would "work the room," introduce myself, and get to know as many people as possible. I was passionate about my organizing work and loved speaking about the connection between our spaces and our well-being. However, each and every time I found that the large crowds mentally drained me.

I knew there had to be a better way. Now I understand using my communication skills through one-on-one connection and building up referrals through my existing network, rather than attempting to mingle among hundreds of people, was the perfect balance for me.

Take a moment to contemplate the relationships in your own life.

Write down the names of the five people you spend the most time with and think about how you can show up better for yourself in these relationships and what the purpose of each of those relationships is within your life.

To what capacity do they hold a presence that supports the most important aspects of your life?

Ask yourself these additional questions:

What can I learn about myself when I interact with this person?

This was an interesting one for me. It actually held so many of the secrets to getting to know myself better.

After an interaction with a friend, I would notice if I was listening to understand or listening to respond. Was I truly showing up for them and their needs? If not, that meant more inner work. If they came to me in confidence *from a place of love* and needed someone to talk to, then that meant I needed to hold space for them. In that moment, the balance would appear. If they had been there to lend an ear for me, then of course I must be just as open and compassionate. This flow of communication is so essential to thriving relationships.

I made an intention to check in with those who had always shown up for me and did my part to ensure I was being mindful of their needs as well. Listening, not interrupting, not judging, and embodying love and compassion.

This then led to my next question.

Am I prioritizing my own needs when I am with this person? Or I am only making it about their needs?

Have you ever found yourself in a relationship in which the other person continuously vents about their day and never asks you about yours? Or maybe you have found yourself doing that to others?

I have had relationships in which it was clear their needs came before mine, however in my desperate attempt for connection I allowed it to be okay. This led to arguments, resentment, and an overall toxic environment when in their presence. I also had to take full responsibility for when I was that person. The one fully absorbed in my own mind, not being present to others' needs.

We don't ever want to be a punching bag for someone as they vent about their day and then take their bad attitude and use it on ourselves. We can lovingly hold space for others, but we cannot allow them to verbally attack or abuse us every time they are upset. And we also can't be the ones who are doing the same to others.

Some of the most difficult, yet freeing, decisions in my life have been made from this place of realization. That relationships are a fundamental piece to our wellness. Who I allowed in, who I gently let go of, and how I learned to repair the relationships that needed tending to along my journey of healing has been life changing.

The relationships around us define us in so many ways. They can shift our energy, offer guidance and support when needed, promote or hinder our growth, allow us to thrive from a level of confidence, empower us to show up as the best version of ourselves, and most importantly allow us the space to be who we are so we can nurture the relationship we have with ourselves.

I believe relationships are a mirror. They reflect to us how we are showing up for ourselves in the world. How we are showing up for ourselves. How we wish to be treated, held, and supported.

If no one told you today: You are worthy of the most incredible, loving, supportive, and thriving relationships in your life. You have everything within you to invite these into your life. You are so incredibly whole by just being you that these healthy, vibrant relationships you are deserving of are simply a reflection of the love you hold inside for yourself.

Would you like to hear an epic love story?

It's the one where you finally, unapologetically, and without hesitation decided you are worthy.

A SPACE FOR JOURNALING AND REFLECTION.

A SPACE FOR JOURNALING AND REFLECTION.

CONCLUSION

"You will cry tears of gratitude when you realize that your healing journey was the path home to yourself."

During my healing from ME/CFS I had the privilege of working with self-expression coach Gemma Hanley. I asked her how much shedding of our former selves she believed was necessary for full healing, when faced with chronic illness. Her response was incredibly honest and beautiful:

> It's an interesting question, and I'm just not sure that there is any shedding of the former "self" to be done at all. Perhaps instead, it is a shedding of what has been acquired from outside of self—that which has been unconsciously or mindlessly bought onboard and then maintained. And that as these acquisitions have never been true "self," they have caused sufficient chaos and pain so as to prompt us to explore exactly that, *"this is not me," "this isn't working as I would like it to," "this triggers disharmony for me," "I'm not so sure this is my path."*

If I was to then shift my answer to the question of how much shedding is required of what is *not* yourself.

> ***To me, "full healing" is a lifestyle. It's the devotion of an individual to discovering their truth in each season of the ever-evolving experience we call life. Embedded within health, relationships, purpose, career, money, and play. Therefore, my answer is as much as is sensed and shifted into conscious awareness from the allowing of all of who we are.***

If you made it to this part of the book, thank you. We've been on a journey together as I have vulnerably shared my deepest truths and the self-care practices that changed my life. So many of these thoughts were at one point scribbled words in my journals that sit next to my bed and are piled high on bookshelves. They were random thoughts that spilled from my mind while in flight and landed on the notes app on my iPhone. Or they were thoughts swirling around in my head. I somehow managed to create this book of truths and healing for you from a place of love.

The chronic illness that tried to swallow me whole was my catalyst for change. I traced back the steps I had taken throughout my life and realized when writing this book that I had been walking the path others had laid out for me. I was never truly tired. I was lost, uninspired, scared, and hiding. And my body let me know.

What a gift to have been given.

I don't believe we should move through life without sharing something, anything, that has profoundly impacted our lives for the better. I believe in storytelling as the one of the most important ways to connect to others, so others know they are not alone.

You are not alone.

Wherever you are in your journey, please keep going. You are exactly where you need to be. This dance you do to protect your heart, to play small, to live outside of yourself, is not meant to be your path to take. You deserve to be fully alive while you are in this human experience.

Feel things. When they are heavy, I know you may want to put them down and run. But lift them close to your heart instead. Ask yourself, "What grows here?" And as they become lighter, carry that light with you through each moment.

Remember that life is happening for you, not at you or around you. For you. Allow it to be the beautiful example of the raw *truth* of who you are.

Here's to claiming ourselves as worthy, beautiful, and whole beings. Unapologetically, as we are and always were.

Welcome home.

ACKNOWLEDGMENTS

I had "published author" on my first vision board fifteen years ago. I could have never envisioned what the process of book writing would look or feel like. Writing *The Unbecoming* was a vulnerable process, one I could not have completed without the support, guidance, and help of many individuals. There is nothing more beautiful than support of those who ask nothing in return.

To the team at CFS Health. Toby Morrison, Gemma Hanley, Dr. Olivia Lessar, and Erin Enright. There are many in my life who did not witness the depths of my darkest days moving through my chronic illness as you all did. The work you do is profound and life changing. Thank you for your help in allowing me to rediscover who I am.

To the incredible team at New Degree Press for the endless access to resources that help in the writing process and for providing me with the confidence and motivation to keep going. Namely my editors, Kaity Van Riper and Benay Stein. You truly opened my eyes to becoming a better writer. A priceless gift.

To my friend Joanna Read who offered her beautiful insight and words of wisdom to this book without hesitation. Your spirit is contagious and I am so grateful for your light.

To those who believed in the book and supported me before the words were sent to print by supporting me in the presale of *The Unbecoming*. Thank you. Heather Barrakad, Louise Frueh, Charlie Bennion, Laura Mahan, Stuart Bryan, Kira Sushkoff-Nguyen, Karen Rand Anderson, Eveline Sperling, Elizabeth Carlson, Helen Moore, Wendy Lewis, Jo-ann Donnelly, Christine Izzi, Kate Giammarco, Nikki Groom, Megan Oliver, Tricia Flori, Sherri Palumbo, Kristen Saunders, Phyllis DeMaio, Gina Armstrong, Patsy Kenney, Christine Barrett, Lisa Giammarco, Michelle Giammarco, Robert Giammarco, Cesare Giammarco, Angela Giammarco, Peter Giammarco, Jessica Rainey, Janice Moore, and my soul sister Ami Flori.

APPENDIX

INTRODUCTION

Walker, Pete. "Shrinking the Inner Critic in Complex PTSD." October 2009. http://www.pete-walker.com/pdf/ShrinkingTheCritic.pdf.

CHAPTER 1

"Your Stone Age Brain (CYP)." *Psychology Tools*. Accessed on September 1, 2021. https://www.psychologytools.com/resource/your-stone-age-brain-cyp.

CHAPTER 3

Friedman, Kenneth, J. "Advances in ME/CFS: Past, Present, and Future." *Frontiers in Pediatrics,* April 18, 2019.
https://doi.org/10.3389/fped.2019.00131.

Hay, L. Louise. "You Can Heal Your Life." Carlsbad, CA: Hay House Inc., 1984.

CHAPTER 4

Lee-Chiong, Dr. Teofilo. "Sleep Smart: Bolstering Immunity with better sleep." Phillips. May 20, 2020.
https://www.usa.philips.com/a-w/about/news/archive/standard/news/articles/20200520-sleep-smart-bolstering-immunity-with-better-sleep.html.

Walker, Matthew. *Why We Sleep: The New Science of Sleep and Dreams*. NY: Penguin Random House, 2017.

CHAPTER 5

Brook, Annie, Ph,D. "Heal Anxiety Related to Birth Trauma in Infants and Adults." Colorado School of Somatic Studies. April 14, 2014.
https://anniebrook.com/heal-anxiety-from-birth-trauma.

Mann, Jenn. Mind-Body Practitioner. Co-founder of CFS School. https://www.chronicfatigueschool.com.

Williams, Anthony. *Medical Medium Celery Juice: The Most Powerful Medicine of our Time Healing Millions Worldwide.* Carlsbad, CA: Hay House, Inc., 2019.

CHAPTER 6

Brown, Brene. *Dare to Lead: Brave Work. Tough Conversations. Whole Hearts.* NY: Random House, 2019.

McAndrew, Frank T. "Why are High School Memories Burned into our Brains?" *The Guardian,* June 2016.
https://www.theguardian.com/commentisfree/2016/jun/02/high-school-memories-teenagers.

CHAPTER 10

Wilson, Edward O. *Biophilia: The Human Bond with Other Species.* Cambridge, Mass.: Harvard University Press, 1986.

CHAPTER 11

Gould, Wendy Rose. "What are Sound Baths? The Healing Power of Sound." Very Well Mind. Accessed June 30, 2020.
https://www.verywellmind.com/what-are-sound-baths-4783501.

Out of this World Integratron. "About: The History of the Integratron." Accessed December 2019.
https://www.integratron.com/history-about.

Printed in Great Britain
by Amazon